teach yourself®

sudoku

james pitts

For over 60 years, more than 40 million people have learnt over 750 subjects the **teach yourself** way, with impressive results.

be where you want to be with **teach yourself**

For UK order enquiries: please contact Bookpoint Ltd, 130 Milton Park, Abingdon, Oxon OX14 4SB. Telephone: +44 (0) 1235 827720. Fax: +44 (0) 1235 400454. Lines are open 09.00–18.00, Monday to Saturday, with a 24-hour message answering service. Details about our titles and how to order are available at www.teachyourself.co.uk

For USA order enquiries: please contact McGraw-Hill Customer Services, PO Box 545, Blacklick, OH 43004-0545, USA. Telephone: 1-800-722-4726. Fax: 1-614-755-5645.

For Canada order enquiries: please contact McGraw-Hill Ryerson Ltd, 300 Water St, Whitby, Ontario L1N 9B6, Canada. Telephone: 905 430 5000. Fax: 905 430 5020.

Long renowned as the authoritative source for self-guided learning – with more than 40 million copies sold worldwide – the **teach yourself** series includes over 300 titles in the fields of languages, crafts, hobbies, business, computing and education.

British Library Cataloguing in Publication Data: a catalogue record for this title is available from the British Library.

Library of Congress Catalog Card Number: on file.

First published in UK 2005 by Hodder Education, 338 Euston Road, London, NW1 3BH.

First published in US 2005 by Contemporary Books, a Division of the McGraw-Hill Companies, 1 Prudential Plaza, 130 East Randolph Street, Chicago, IL 60601 USA.

This edition published 2005.

Typeset by Transet Limited, Coventry, England.
Printed in Great Britain for Hodder Education, a division of Hodder Headline, 338 Euston Road, London NW1 3BH, by Cox & Wyman Ltd, Reading, Berkshire.

Hodder Headline's policy is to use papers that are natural, renewable and recyclable products and made from wood grown in sustainable forests. The logging and manufacturing processes are expected to conform to the environmental regulations of the country of origin.

Impression number 10 9 8 7 6 5 4 3
Year 2010 2009 2008 2007 2006 2005

contents

introduction

In this chapter you will learn:

- about how Sudoku became the craze it is today
- the rules and jargon of Sudoku
- tactics and techniques
- where to find Sudoku on the internet.

Sudoku roots

The origin of Sudoku, sometimes spelled *Su doku*, can be traced back to eighteenth century Europe and the Swiss mathematician, Leonhard Euler, who devised a number puzzle called 'Latin Squares': a grid of 81 squares in which no row nor column can contain the same number twice.

During the late 1970s Latin Squares resurfaced in America under the name 'Number Place', when the specialist puzzle publisher Dell printed it in puzzle magazine *Math Puzzles and Logic Problems*.

Tokyo publisher Nikoli, who came across the puzzle in America, subsequently imported it to Japan for their own puzzle paper *Monthly Nikolist* in 1984. The puzzle was introduced as 'Suuji Wa Dokushin Ni Kagiru' but was subsequently abbreviated to 'Sudoku', meaning 'solitary number'.

These early puzzles were hardly the resounding success they are today until two major improvements were made to the concept in 1986, making the game more difficult and guaranteeing the popularity of the puzzle. The grid was subdivided into nine 3 × 3 blocks – as with the rows and columns, no block could contain the same number twice, while to further increase the challenge there were to be no more than 30 given clues.

The improved brainteaser became an overnight success in Japan, where a new craze was born.

Did you know?

In Japan, number puzzles are more common than word puzzles, as the language does not lend itself easily to crosswords.

Sudoku fever

The current phenomenon, however, can be accredited to Wayne Gould, a retired judge from New Zealand, who discovered Sudoku in a bookstore in Tokyo in 1997.

> As soon as I saw the grid with the empty squares, I felt very tempted to fill them in.
>
> *Wayne Gould, the Observer, 15 May 2005*

Gould developed a computer program that generates new puzzles instantly, working at varying levels of difficulty. He pitched his brainteasing discovery to the London *Times* who, intrigued, started publishing the game in November 2004.

> I'm surprised and amazed at how popular it has become and I can't really explain it.
>
> *Wayne Gould, the Observer, 15 May 2005*

Sudoku not only is now the most popular puzzle in Japan, where dedicated magazines regularly reach a circulation of 600,000, but has also become immensely popular in British newspapers, and has spread like wildfire across the internet.

Today the game is being called the 'Rubik's cube of the twenty-first century', and has been compared to chess and cryptic crosswords for its ability to refine logical thinking and reasoning skills. Some educators have even suggested it be added to the school curriculum, while certain medical experts recommend a Sudoku a day to stave off such conditions as Alzheimer's disease.

The need to know

1 The rules

Sudoku should be solved by lateral thinking alone; it should never involve the use of trial and error.

The rules are hardly complicated.

> **What to do**
>
> Complete the grid so that every row, every column and every 3 × 3 box contains the digits 1 to 9.

It really is that simple but – as you have probably realised – Sudoku is not. The grids rated 'fiendish' or 'very hard', really are; however, keep the simple principle of the rules at the forefront of your mind and you'll be competing with the best of them in no time.

Guessing should not be an option: some experts believe that to construct a Sudoku in such a manner as to make guessing necessary is very poor form. It is a test of your logic and reasoning abilities, not of your ability to toss a coin. It is probably this principle alone that has made this puzzle such a success. Unlike in so many other areas of life, there is no room for chance.

Top tip

Although Sudoku does not require the use of arithmetic or mathematics, being able to count to nine can prove helpful.

2 The jargon

The world of Sudoku has, inevitably, developed a language of its own to describe the distinct parts.

- **Grid**: the complete Sudoku square with 81 numbers in a 9 × 9 layout.
- **Cell** or **Unit**: a single space for a number.
- **Column**: a vertical line of nine numbers.
- **Row**: a horizontal collection of nine cells.
- **Line**: could be either a row or a column.
- **Block** or **Quadrant**: a 3 × 3 collection of cells of which there are nine in a Sudoku grid.
- **Area**: nine cells as a block, a column or a row.
- **Towers**: three vertical cells in a block; each block has three towers.
- **Stacks**: a vertical arrangement of three blocks – there are three stacks in a Sudoku puzzle.
- **Bands**: a horizontal arrangement of three blocks – there are three bands in a Sudoku puzzle.
- **Givens** or **Clues**: the numbers provided at the start of a puzzle: the number of givens varies from puzzle to puzzle;

typically a more difficult puzzle will have fewer given numbers, sometimes as few as 22, while easier puzzles will have anywhere up to 30 givens.

- **Unknown:** a blank cell.
- **Candidate:** a possible number for a cell.
- **Pencil marks:** temporary clues or candidates written as a reminder in the corner of a cell.
- **Pairs:** identical pencil marks in two different cells.
- **Singleton:** situation where only a single number could possibly go in a cell.

3 The references

Cells are often identified by a grid reference, starting with the row number and then the column: for example, cell 5,5 is the cell at the very centre of the grid. Blocks are also identified in this manner: block 1,3, for instance, is the one at the top right. Blocks are also numbered in reading order, starting with block 1 in the top left and block 9 at the bottom right.

Top tip

A variation on this method of cells and block numbering, which has become very popular on the internet, is to use the same grid reference as above but enclose cell references in round brackets – ( ) – and block references in square brackets – [ ].

4 Technique, tactics, tips

Enough procrastination: grab a decent sharp pencil, an eraser, a fresh cup of coffee or a glass of wine if you prefer and we'll get started.

Finding your first cell

There are lots of techniques that will help you complete a Sudoku. Some techniques are obvious, some others not so. I will present you with various methods for solving those elusive empty squares in a 'show and tell' approach that is easy to follow.

Let's examine this Sudoku grid below.

2			3		1		8	
		7	2					
	8			5				3
3	1							
		6	1		8	2		
							1	4
7				3			9	
					5	7		
	6		8		2			1

We'll start with the bottom three blocks, also called a band. Do you see the 7 in block 7 and another in block 9? And did you also notice that there is no 7 in block 8?

							1	4
7				3			9	
					5	7		
	6		8		2			1

We know that each block, row and column can only have a single 7 in it. There must be a 7 in row 9, and as blocks 7 and 9 already have a 7 in, the only place it could possibly go is in cell 5 of row 9, between the 8 and the 2.

							1	4
7				3			9	
					5	7		
	6		8	7	2			1

Congratulations, that's the first cell done. Only another 54 to go!

Now we will consider four boxes at the same time, using a variation of the technique above to eliminate another number. Think about blocks 1, 2 and 3 and the number 3.

2			3		1		8	
		7	2					
	8			5				3
3	1							
		6	1		8	2		
							1	4

We can see that row 1 block 2 and row 1 block 3 both have the number 3 placed, leaving only two places in block 1 where it can go, locations (2,1) and (2,2).

By using the 3 in block 4 we can erase the possibility that the 3 could be in the first column – so it must be in the second, at position (2,2). 53 left!

2			3		1		8	
	3	7	2					
	8			5				3
3	1							
		6	1		8	2		
							1	4

By building on our success we can complete all the 3s in the grid. It is by exploiting each of these little victories that we can work our way to a complete solution and the satisfaction of a job well done.

Can you place the 1 in block 8? Or the 8 in block 2?

Tactics!

1 Pencil marking

Very few of us have either the mental capacity or the memory to remember where all the given clues in the grid are, let alone all the possibilities or candidates that each cell may contain. The process of writing little clues in the corner of each box is called pencil marking.

A pencil mark is a note of a possible value for that cell. It is often a better strategy to go for an all or nothing approach when marking a cell, so leave it blank or list all the candidates for it. If you successfully find the value of a cell, scan that row, column and block, and eliminate it from all the pencil marks that may exist. Eventually you will have eliminated enough pencil marks to start finding singletons.

Top tip

Remember to keep the pencil marks up to date and accurate or you'll find yourself quite swiftly in hot Sudoku water.

2 Are there any singletons here?

Finding singletons is what Sudoku is all about. It is that deduction in logic where the only possible result for a cell is a single number, or as it's called in Sudoku, a singleton.

One of the easiest techniques is just to start counting. Pick a likely-looking square and start counting from one, keeping a mental tally. Say to yourself with your finger or pencil on the cell, 'Are there any 1s in this block, row or column?, any 2s? 3s?' If the answer is 'no', just jot down a little pencil mark in the corner of that cell.

If, after all the other possibilities have been reviewed, there remains only a single pencil mark for that cell, you have found its value. But this can be expanded further. If a pencil marked number appears only once in a row then that must be its value regardless of how many pencil marks are actually in that cell. If it is the only 6, for example, marked in the row, then that must be it. You have found a singleton. This technique can be applied to columns and blocks just as easily.

3 Pinpoint the pairs

A pairing situation is where you have two cells that both have the same two pencil marks.

Finding a pair of numbers is a very useful technique that you will use in most intermediate and higher rated Sudoku puzzles. In the partial Sudoku grid below we can use a technique to eliminate some pencil marks and find a lone number.

12	12	9	3	4	5	6	7	8
3	4	5						
126	12678	12678						
7								
8								

Look at cells (1,1) and (1,2): the pencil marks 1 and 2 within those cells are the only two possibilities remaining on that row. The answer for the first two cells may be the 1 and then the 2 or the 2 and then the 1 – we don't know yet because we don't have enough information.

But we do know these must be the cells that contain 1 and 2 for that row, therefore they can't go anywhere else in that first block.

We can thus eliminate candidates 1 and 2 from all other cells in that block.

This leaves us with a singleton at location (3,1): 6.

> **Top tip**
>
> In Sudoku, knowing which numbers go where is just as important as knowing which numbers don't go where. This is something we will look at more in the advanced section.

12	12	9	3	4	5	6	7	8
3	4	5						
6	78	78						
7								
8								

This technique can be used on both rows and columns. It can also be employed in situations where you have more than two pencil marks in an equal number of unknown cells.

In our example, although we did not manage to work out where 1 and 2 go, we did discover where they do not go.

Advanced techniques

The basic technique as shown above will get you a long way towards solving most puzzles but you will start to struggle on the hard or difficult puzzles in the last third of this book. This is when you need to learn the advanced techniques. These methods may at first require some determination, but your perseverance will pay off eventually.

1 Stack and band elimination

A very good attempt has been made to complete the Sudoku pictured below with straightforward elimination, but the solver has reached an apparent dead end. None of the techniques shown above are working and, in a desperate attempt to find a singleton, lots of pencil marks have been filled in.

Help, however, is at hand – we can achieve elimination, by block, of candidate cells by considering the bands and stacks (forgotten what they are? Look at 'The jargon', above).

5	9	1	7	8	2			6
2	3	4	1	5	6	7	8	9
6	7	8	3	4	9			
17	2	5679	4	3				8
3	15	579	6		8			
4	8	569		2			7	
17	16	2	8	679	3	1469	5	147
8	4	3567	59	1	57	2	369	37
9	156	3567	2	67	4	8	136	137

The sheer number of pencil marks in row 9 of block 7 suggests that they are far from useful – but in fact they are. Let's look at the 5s in row 9.

Row 9 has only two locations where a 5 can go, (9,2) and (9,3); both of these are in the same block. So, we know that row 9 must have a 5 in it somewhere and it must be in one of those 2 cells: therefore, a 5 can't go anywhere else in block 7, so we can eliminate the 5 in (8,3).

Still, that didn't reveal anything to help complete this grid; so let's look at column 2. Do you notice the same situation occurring, in block 7 again, but this time in the columns?

5	9	1	7	8	2			6
2	3	4	1	5	6	7	8	9
6	7	8	3	4	9			
17	2	5679	4	3				8
3	15	579	6		8			
4	8	569		2			7	
17	16	2	8	679	3	1469	5	147
8	4	3567	59	1	57	2	369	37
9	156	3567	2	67	4	8	136	137

The 6 can only appear in two locations within column 2 and, again, both are in block 7, so by applying the same logic as before we can remove the 6 pencil marks from locations (8,3) and (9,3). This leaves us with a singleton 6 at (8,8), and the puzzle unlocks itself again.

This technique shows that viewing the whole grid from time to time is just as useful as the micro management of rows, columns and blocks.

2 More on pairs

> How often have I said to you that when you have eliminated the impossible, whatever remains, however improbable, must be the truth?
>
> *Sherlock Holmes, The Sign of Four (1890)*

Spotting a pair is a very useful method for clearing up pencil marks and progressing towards a complete solution. Consider this portion of a Sudoku grid opposite.

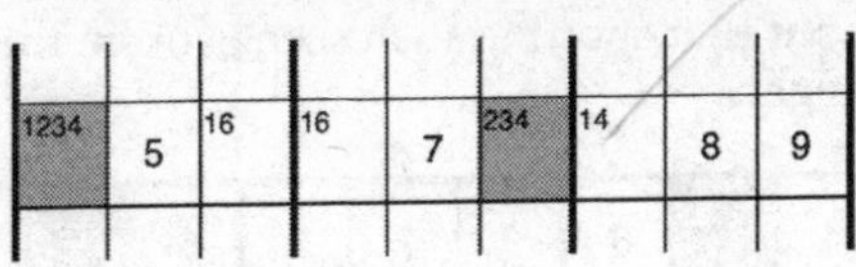

On an initial glance it does not look like the pencil marks reveal a candidate we could use. But this situation is another form of the pair's method we described above; it's just well hidden.

Do you see the candidates 2 and 3? They can only go in two locations in that row, cell 1 and cell 6. This means that 1 and 4 cannot go in either of these cells.

So we can erase the 1 and 4 pencil marks from these cells. This then leaves a singleton 4 in cell 7.

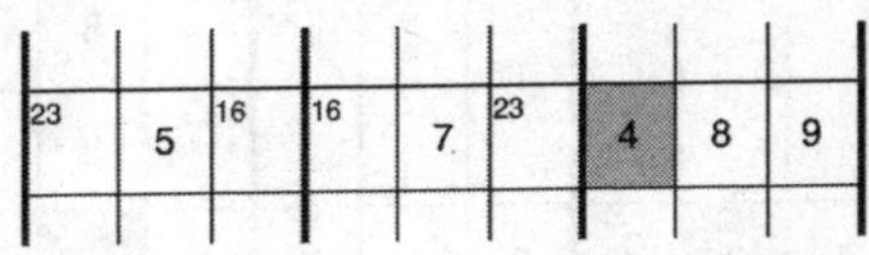

This applies equally well to columns and blocks and, as mentioned in the first section on pairs, this technique can be extended to work with triples and quads.

3 The x-wing

The rather ominous-sounding x-wing allows you to remove extraneous pencil marks in the hope that either a lone number will be revealed or you will advance the candidates to a level where you can apply another technique. It is a method that you probably won't need except for the most fiendishly difficult puzzles (and may prevent you throwing the puzzle out in frustration ...).

Below is a partial Sudoku grid to illustrate the method. It should be pointed out that spotting such scenarios 'in the wild' is a skill in its own right.

4	67	8	9	2	3	5	67	1
						3		2
			1	7	4		69	
							5	
							8	
5	26	4	8	1	7	9	26	3

An 'x-wing' can be applied when four cells form the corners of a rectangle – of any size – and each of the four cells has a common pencil-mark candidate. You can see one of these rectangles formed by the points (1,2), (1,8), (9,8) and (9,2) and with the common candidate 6.

For an x-wing to apply, the pencil marks that create the corners of the rectangle must only appear twice in either the rows or the columns. In our example, this is the case in the top and bottom rows.

A 6 lies in row 1 and row 9 and in columns 2 and 8: it can't go anywhere else in these columns. We can thus eliminate all the 6 candidates from the rest of these columns. In our example, this leaves us with the singleton 9 at position (5,8).

The fog of war

It is very easy not to see the wood for the trees or, in Sudoku terms, the numbers for all the digits. Try not to get bogged down on a single unknown cell – if it's not working perhaps try another technique for a while. If that fails it may be best to take a break, wash the bits of broken pencil from your mouth, unclench your fists, take a deep breath, top the wine glass up and try looking at it a little later with a fresh pair of eyes.

Remember

It is not uncommon for some Sudoku puzzles to take days to complete. There is not a Sudoku that can't be solved ... given enough time.

Similarly, it is possible to be a little over zealous with the pencil marking, leaving the grid as a mess of notes and crossing out. Try to keep it uncluttered and easy to read – pencil mark only when absolutely necessary and always have an eraser handy!

Sudoku technology: computer programs

1 The Sudoku fun widget

If you own a Macintosh computer, distraction is only a keystroke away with the Sudoku fun program for the dashboard (http://www.sudokufun.com/widget.php). It will check your solution for you and, if you get really stuck, will take you to the solution.

2 Pappocom's Sudoku

The Pappocom website (http://www.sudoku.com) has a trial version of a Sudoku program available for download. The program will allow you to 'dub' Sudoku grids into the program and will offer you a hint when you get stuck.

Sudoku websites

Sudoku has become immensely popular on the internet, with an explosion of websites offering the opportunity to play online, join forums and discover solving techniques.

1 Sudoku fun

The Sudoku Fun website (http://www.sudokufun.com) has more challenging puzzles in a day than you could possibly ever complete, but that does not stop many from trying. A leader board with every puzzle shows the successful few to meet the 'Speed Challenge'.

2 Sudoku puzzles by Pappocom

The Pappocom website (http://www.sudoku.com) offers lots of excellent hints and tips for cracking puzzles and has a very helpful forum for discussion with other players.

3 Daily Sudoku

As the name suggests, http://www.dailysudoku.co.uk has a single Sudoku every day for you to print out.

02 beginner

In this chapter you will:

- **complete 42 beginner-level Sudoku.**

Let the fun begin

On the following pages you will find 156 Sudoku puzzles of varying difficulty. They have been rated beginner, novice, intermediate and expert. As you progress you will have to employ the techniques I have described and you may have to devise some of your own. All of the puzzles have logical solutions – you won't have to guess (although you can if you wish: just keep your pencil and eraser handy).

Best of luck and enjoy!

James Pitts, 2005

19 beginner 02

			2		3			
1				6			8	
6		9			8	2		
2		4					9	
	8	6				4	5	
	9					1		3
		1	6			8		5
	4			1				6
			7		2			

1

Continuous effort, not strength or intelligence, is the key to unlocking our potential.
Liane Cardes

20 beginner **02**

5		2				6		7
			2					8
4		9	5					
	1	5		3	6			
			9		1			
			7	5		3	1	
					5	8		6
8					4			
9		4				5		1

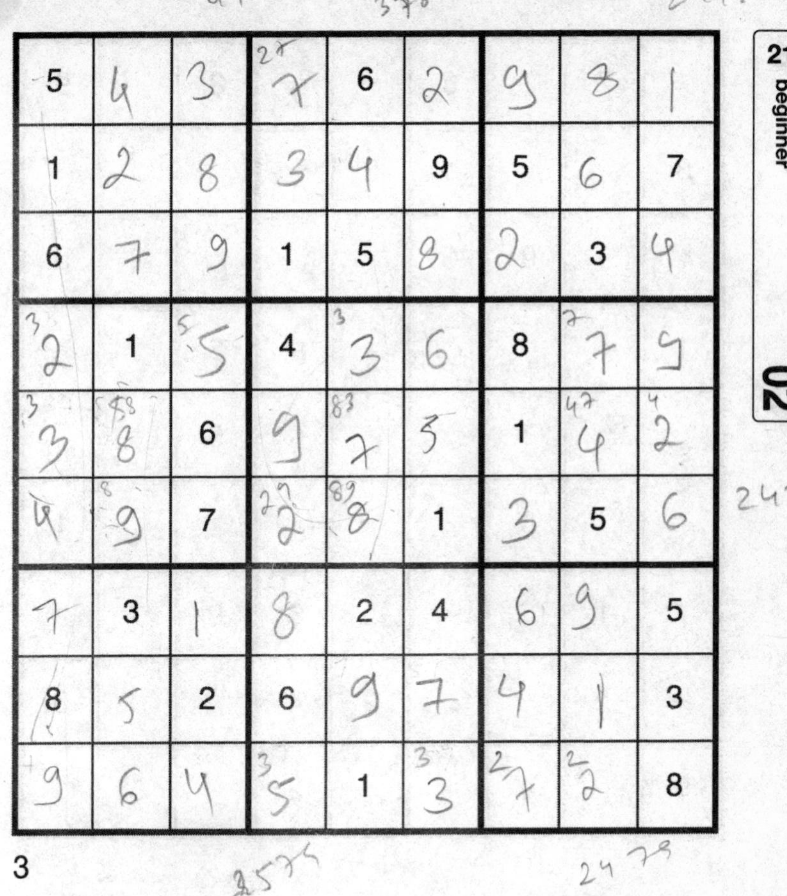

3

There is divinity in odd numbers…
William Shakespeare

22 beginner 02

	7		6			3		9
3			1	2				
		9	3				2	5
1						8		
		7				5		
		8						1
7	1				3	9		
				9	4			6
9		4			2		5	

23 beginner 02

7			4		2			9
				8				
5	8				7	2		
	1	5		3				8
		7				4		
4				7		6	2	
		1	8				7	2
				1				
9			2		6			1

24 beginner 02

			7	5				
		8	1			5		
	7			6			3	4
						6	9	
4		5				3		2
	9	7						
7	2			3			4	
		3			7	9		
				2	4			

25 beginner 02

1	9				5	2		
	4			3				9
				6		1	3	
3					6	7	9	
	8	9	5					2
	3	1		8				
8				1			7	
		4	7				1	3

O Logic: born gatekeeper to the Temple of Science, victim of capricious destiny: doomed hitherto to be the drudge of pedants: come to the aid of thy master, Legislation.

Jeremy Bentham

26 beginner 02

4			7				6	
			2					
7	8	9						5
	1	4	3					8
			9	8	1			
5					4	1	3	
6						8	5	3
					2			
	7				3			2

27 beginner

02

3					6	7	8	
		8			3			
				7		1	2	
1	3			5			9	
	9			8			5	4
	2	1		9				
			6			9		
	5	6	7					1

28 beginner 02

7					1	6		
		3		5			8	
	6	8		7	9			
2			6			4	9	
	9	7			5			2
			9	4		8	7	
	5			1		9		
		4	5					1

10

Do not worry about your difficulties in mathematics.
I can assure you mine are still greater.
Albert Einstein

29 beginner 02

5			7					
1				6		5		9
					9	1	2	
2		5			6		9	
	8						4	
	9		1			6		3
	4	1	9					
8		2		4				7
					5			2

		8				4	7	
	2		3					9
		9	2	6			3	
				3				8
3			7		1			4
5				2				
	4			5	3	8		
8					6		4	
	6	3				5		

12

A little nonsense now and then is relished by the wisest men.
Roald Dahl

31 beginner

			4				8	
	2	6				4	5	
			5	6		1		3
			6			7		
3	4						1	6
		9			7			
7		1		8	5			
	5	2				9	3	
	6				3			

13

32 beginner 02

		8			3			
	3	5			9	6		
2	4							5
3		2			6			7
	8						5	
5			1			3		6
7							8	3
		3	7			9	6	
			8			7		

14

Sudoku Addict Alert! I've got an hour's commute into work and back again so am getting through a lot of puzzles.
Tom

33 beginner 02

			8	3	4	1		
		4	2					
	8	9						
	1			4	5			
3	5						1	2
			7	1			6	
						6	2	
					1	9		
		3	5	2	6			

5	2	7			4			
1							8	
		9			7		4	
2	1		6					
3			8		9			2
					2		6	7
	4		3			8		
	5							3
			7			5	1	4

16

Numbers are intellectual witnesses that belong only to mankind.
Honore de Balzac

35 beginner 02

				8	7	6		
1			2	3			7	
	8	9				2		
2		3						
	6						5	
						4		6
		1				7	8	
	5			6	3			1
		4	8	1				

17

There can never be surprises in logic.
Ludwig Wittgenstein

36 beginner 02

		1		5		2	9	
			1					
	8	9			7			4
				3		7		9
			9		2			
6		8		7				
7			3			4	5	
					5			
	5	6		2		8		

37 beginner

02

		4				8		1
	2			7				
6			1	5		2		
2					6		9	
	6	7				1	4	
	8		5					6
		1		6	4			7
				9			5	
8		6				4		

8	1			2		9		
					9			8
6			3					
	2		5		4		8	
3								2
	9		2		1		5	
					2			7
7			9					
		3		4			6	1

20

Reason's last step is the recognition that there are an infinite number of things which are beyond it.
Blaise Pascal

39 beginner 02

				9		4		7
		4	3	5			8	
			4				2	
2	1				4	7		
3								4
		8	7				1	5
	3				2			
	4			7	5	9		
9		5		4				

40 beginner 02

1		6	3					
		4		5			8	9
			2					5
	1			7		4		
		7	9		8	5		
		8		3			7	
6					3			
8	4			6		9		
					4	3		2

22

Sudoku Addict Alert! I had to get off at that stop!
Ahmed

41 beginner 02

3					8			
1				4		7		9
		9				3	4	
2	1						9	
	7		8		6		2	
	9						5	7
	3	1				8		
8		2		1				4
			7					1

42 beginner 02

				8				
	3	6	1	4				
5			2					6
	2	5				6	9	
	4		8		9		1	
	9	8				4	3	
7					3			5
				2	1	9	7	
				5				

43 beginner 02

	3		5	9	2			
1							6	
		9	1					4
	1		6	3				7
	7						4	
6				7	1		5	
7					3	9		
	5							3
			7	2	4		8	

				4	8	1		7
1	4	6				5		
5					9			
3		2		5			9	
	9			8		4		2
			6					5
		3				9	2	6
9		4	8	2				

26

Each problem that I solved became a rule which served afterwards to solve other problems.
René Descartes

45 beginner

02

6		4					7	8
	2	7			9			6
					7			3
			6				8	
	7			5			1	
	9				2			
7			8					
8			1			3	9	
9	6					8		1

46 beginner 02

		6	2				8	
		5		4		6	7	
	7				9			
	1	4		3	6			
			9		1			
			4	2		3	5	
			8				6	
	5	2		1		9		
	6				4	8		

47 beginner 02

	2		5		7		4	
1		5			6		8	
6						2		
2						5		
	5		8		1		2	
		9						3
		1						7
	6		9			8		4
	9		7		5		1	

29

[Mathematics] is an independent world
Created out of pure intelligence.
William Wordsworth

	9	4			7			6
	2		3		6			9
		8						
2	1						9	
4			9		5			1
	8						7	3
						3		
8			4		3		1	
9			5			8	4	

	7		9		4			
	4			2				
6		9				1	2	
2			4	3				8
		7				5		
5				1	6			2
	2	1				9		6
				9			1	
			8		1		3	

49 beginner

50 beginner 02

5			9	4			8	
		4	2		8			
		9						5
	1					7		8
	6						1	
4		8					3	
6						9		
			4		3	1		
	7			1	5			4

32

Whenever you can, count.
Sir Francis Galton

			2	5				4
		7					6	
		9				1	2	3
1					4			9
		6	8		2	4		
4			5					2
6	3	1				2		
	5					8		
9				2	1			

33

Mathematics seems to endow one with something like a new sense.
Charles Darwin

52 beginner 02

6	4	7					9	
			2	4		6		
	8							5
3	1				6			9
			5		8			
5			3				6	7
7							3	
		3		1	4			
	6					8	5	1

53 beginner 02

6								8
		5	1			4	6	
	7		5		9			
		6		3			9	
3		7				2		5
	8			1		3		
			6		3		8	
	5	3			4	6		
9								2

35

It is the man who carefully advances step by step, with his mind becoming wider and wider – and progressively better able to grasp any theme or situation – persevering in what he knows to be practical, and concentrating his thought upon it, who is bound to succeed in the greatest degree.

Alexander Graham Bell

54 beginner

02

			3			8		
		7		4	8		6	
5				7	9		3	
		4				7	9	
3								2
	8	9				1		
	2		6	9				5
	4		7	5		9		
		6			4			

55 beginner

02

				4	9		3	
1					6	7		
	5		2		8			
		3				5		8
	8	6				3	2	
5		7				4		
			6		2		5	
		2	9					3
	6		7	3				

56 beginner

02

7								
	2	4			8			9
		9		5	7		3	
				3	5			
	5	7				4	2	
			1	7				
	4		6	2		7		
8			7			9	1	
								2

38

Mathematics, rightly viewed, possesses not only truth,
but supreme beauty.
Bertrand Russell

57 beginner

02

	7		4			8		
		4		5		6		
3			6					4
	1	3					9	8
			9		3			
5	8					4	6	
6					2			7
		2		3		9		
		5			4		1	

58 beginner 02

	6						2	
2		4	1		9			
		9		5		1	3	
	1		4			8		
			6		8			
		8			3		4	
	4	1		3		9		
			9		1	6		3
	7						5	

40

5	4			6		2		
1					8	6		
6	7			2	9			
	1							8
			9		7			
4							3	
			5	9			6	4
		2	6					7
		4		7			2	3

59 beginner

02

60 beginner

02

		4			5		2	
2			1				8	9
				3	9			
		6						8
	5	7				2	1	
4						5		
			9	7				
7	6				1			3
	9		5			4		

03 novice

In this chapter you will:

- complete 44 novice-level Sudoku.

62 novice 03

		9	2	6	8			
2	3			5				
	7		3					
	1	2						8
	8						7	
5						4	1	
					3		5	
				1			6	2
			7	2	4	8		

		2	8		9		7	
						6	8	9
				5				4
2			5			3		
	7	6				1	5	
		8			2			7
7				8				
8	4	3						
	6		7		1	8		

63 novice

03

A fool thinks himself to be wise, but a wise man
knows himself to be a fool.
William Shakespeare

			5			2		
		5				7	8	
6	7			2			4	
	1			3		5		8
			9		1			
4		8		5			7	
	3			6			2	7
	6	2				9		
		4			5			

45

65 novice 03

6								7
	2		3				8	9
		9	2		6	1		
					5	7		
3		7				2		1
		8	7					
		1	8		2	3		
8	6				3		5	
9								2

In mathematics you don't understand things.
You just get used to them.
Johann von Neumann

66 novice 03

8	3			9	2			
	2				6			9
5			4					
		5				4		8
	7		9		4		5	
4		8				3		
					9			7
7			8				1	
			7	4			6	2

67 novice 03

	4			9	6			
1					5	7	8	
		9				3		
3		1		2			9	
	9			8		4		2
		3				8		
	2	4	7					3
			8	3			6	

Everything should be made as simple as possible,
but not simpler.
Albert Einstein

68 novice 03

				2	9		8	
	2	3			8			
		9	3			1		
2				3			9	
	6		9		1		5	
	9			7				3
		1			6	8		
			7			9	6	
	7		8	4				

49

69 novice

03

			7					
		6			9	5	7	
	8			5		1		
	1	5		3			8	
3			8		5			2
	9			2		6	5	
		1		7			2	
	5	2	4			9		
					2			

1			3		7			4
	3			5	6			
5			2					
		2				6		8
	8						1	
6		7				4		
					4			3
			6	2			7	
9			7		8			1

51

As far as the laws of mathematics refer to reality, they are not certain; and as far as they are certain, they do not refer to reality.
Albert Einstein

71 novice

03

			2				4	8
					8			9
	5		6		9		2	
2	1	4						
		6				2		
						3	6	4
	3		9		2		8	
7			3					
8	9				1			

				8				
	4	5			6		8	
	7		3			1		
2	1		6	7				
			9		5			
				1	8		6	3
		1			2		5	
	5		7			9	4	
				5				

53

'Obvious' is the most dangerous word in mathematics.
Eric Temple Bell

1			2	5	3			
	3							
5		9	4		7			
				2		7		9
4		7				6		5
6		8		1				
			5		6	2		8
							7	
			8	7	2			1

73 novice 03

7		1	4			8		
2					8			9
				6		1	3	
1			3			7	9	
	9	8			2			1
	1	2		9				
8			6					7
		4			3	6		2

75 novice 03

					1			
1	2				8	5		
6	8	9		5				
2		3			6		9	
	7						3	
	9		2			6		4
				9		8	5	2
		2	7				6	1
			8					

76 novice 03

2						9		
1			2	4	9			
6	8			5	7			
	1		4				8	
		6				1		
	9				3		4	
			5	3			9	6
			6	9	1			7
		4						5

57

Perfect numbers, like perfect men, are very rare.
René Descartes

77 novice

03

	9	1	3					
2		6			8		5	
4			5					
			4			8		
3	4						6	1
		9			7			
					4			5
	5		7			9		6
					3	7	1	

78 novice

03

		3			6		8	
1	2			4				9
				5	9			
	1				5			8
3								6
4			7				5	
			9	2				
7				8			4	1
	9		6			3		

79 novice

03

	1		9				3	8
2					8		7	9
5		9						
					6			
		6	2		9	4		
			5					
						2		3
8	5		7					6
9	6				4		5	

80 novice 03

		8	7			2		6
2			1					9
					8		4	
1	2					6		
	8	6				4	1	
		7					5	2
	4		9					
8					3			1
9		3			7	5		

81 novice 03

	4		6				3	
	2							9
				3		2		5
2	1			4				7
			9		7			
4				8			6	2
7		1		9				
8							1	
	6				5		2	

82 novice 03

7					1	6		
			4			5		8
	8			5		1	3	
2		6			4			
3								6
			6			3		5
	3	1		9			2	
8		2			3			
		4	1					3

Mathematics began to seem too much like puzzle solving.
Physics is puzzle solving, too, but of puzzles created by nature,
not by the mind of man.
Maria Goeppert Mayer

							7	1
1	2			4			6	
	8	9	1					
2		3			5			
4								2
			2			1		6
					4	8	2	
	4			3			9	7
9	6							

64

God does arithmetic.
Karl Friedrich Gauss

9	2				4			
				6				
5		7	3				2	
	1			3	6		9	
		6	8		2	4		
	8		1	7			3	
	4				3	8		5
				4				
			7				4	2

65

85 novice 03

			6	4			5	7
	7							8
				7		1	2	3
		4					8	
3			2		7			4
	9					2		
7	2	1		3				
8							7	
9	5			8	2			

86 novice 03

	4			6				
1		5						
			1	7		2		5
2		3	4				9	
	7	6				3	5	
	8				7	4		6
6		1		8	5			
						9		3
				2			6	

87 novice 03

7				3	2	6		
	2			5			8	9
		8				2		
					7			8
3			2		4			1
4			5					
		1				9		
8	5			4			6	
		4	6	2				3

68

The mathematician has reached the highest
rung on the ladder of human thought.
Havelock Ellis

novice 88

03

	7	5		4				2
1					9			
	8					1		4
			4	2		7		
4				9				5
		8		7	1			
7		1					5	
			6					3
9				5		4	2	

89 novice 03

		2			1			
		6					7	8
	8			5			2	
2		5	3		4			
3				2				1
			5		7	2		6
	2			4			8	
8	5					7		
			6			3		

	6			8				
	3		2		6			9
2	4	8				3		
		2	4	5			9	
	8			6	1	2		
		1				9	7	4
7			6		4		1	
				1			6	

71

... from the time of Kepler to that of Newton, and from Newton to Hartley, not only all things in external nature, but the subtlest mysteries of life and organization, and even of the intellect and moral being, were conjured within the magic circle of mathematical formulae.

Samuel Taylor Coleridge

91 novice

03

	4	8						1
1		5	3				7	
			1	2	8			
		3		5		7		
			7		1			
		7		8		4		
			5	6	2			
	5				4	1		7
9						5	3	

							7	4
1		4	3					
				6	8		2	
2				3			8	
		7	8		1	2		
	9			2				1
	3		2	8				
					5	6		7
9	6							

73

omnia apud me mathematica fiunt.
With me everything turns into mathematics.
René Descartes

93 novice

03

				7			6	
		6	2			7	8	
		9			6	2		
2			3	5				
3			4		9			2
				1	2			4
		1	5			8		
	5	2			4	9		
	7			2				

94 novice 03

	9		6			8		5
		4						
		8		7			2	3
					5			8
		7				2		
4			2					
6	1			9		4		
						9		
9		5			4		1	

							9	4
				8		5		
				5	7	1	2	
3			5			7		9
4			2		8			5
5		8			3			6
	2	1	3	6				
		3		2				
9	6							

95 novice 03

96 novice

03

	7	9	5					
1				4	6	7		
3			2					
	1						9	8
		4				2		
6	9						3	
					8			4
		2	9	1				6
					4	8	1	

97 novice 03

		9			8	5	3	
		8			9	2	4	
	1		3				9	
5			6		2			7
	9				4		5	
	2	1	5			9		
	6	5	7			8		

It is a capital mistake to theorize before you have all the evidence.
Sir Arthur Conan Doyle

98 novice 03

8		5			7	2		
	2				6		8	
3						4	5	
	1			3				8
		7				6		
5				1			4	
	4	1						5
	5		9				6	
		3	2			1		4

					3		8	
3	5		1	2				
	8	9		6		1		
2		3						
		4	3		9	2		
						5		4
		1		9		8	5	
				3	5		1	7
	6		8					

99 novice 03

Sudoku Addict Alert! The first time I saw Sudoku was when my mathematics teacher gave everyone in the class one to do. At the time I though it was a bit boring, but much better than a normal math lesson.
Robert

		1	9					
2	3					7		9
	7			3			4	
	2				4	5		8
				8				
5		8	6				3	
	1			9			5	
8		3					2	4
					5	3		

81

Defendit numerus: there is safety in numbers.
Anonymous

101 novice 03

4			7				8	
	2	5		4		6		
				6	9			5
		4						8
5			8		1			2
6						3		
7			9	8				
		2		7		9	1	
	6				4			7

The mathematical sciences particularly exhibit order, symmetry and limitation; and these are the greatest forms of the beautiful.
Aristotle

102 novice 03

3	5		9	6				
	4						8	9
	8				7	2		
			4	7				
		6				3		
				1	2			
		1	6				5	
8	3						6	
				2	3		4	7

103 novice

03

			9				7	1
1						6		
			1	2	8	3		
				6		7	9	
3	8						2	4
	9	7		8				
		1	5	4	9			
		2						7
9	6				2			

7			3					
1			2			7	8	
4		8			9			
	1			3	7		9	
	4						2	
	8		6	1			7	
			9			8		7
	5	3			4			2
					1			3

105 novice 03

				9	2		7	
2		5						
4		9	3			1		
			6	3	5			8
5			2	7	4			
		1			9	8		2
						9		6
	8		4	2				

04 intermediate

In this chapter you will:

- **complete 44 intermediate-level Sudoku.**

107 intermediate 04

7	9	8	3					
1					6			9
		6					2	
		4	6			5		
			5		8			
		9			1	3		
	3					8		
8			1					7
					3	4	6	1

108 intermediate 04

		2		4	7			5
	5				9	4	7	
			5			1		
	1	4		5				
	6						4	
				7		2	3	
		1			3			
	4	3	9				6	
9			6	2		3		

109 intermediate 04

			1	3		8	5	
			4		8		7	9
						1		
2							9	
	8		7		1		4	
	9							6
		1						
8	4		9		3			
	7	5		2	6			

The union of the mathematician with the poet, fervor with measure, passion with correctness, this surely is the ideal.
William James

110 intermediate 04

			1		3			
1				5	6		8	
4	5				9		3	
		4				6	9	
		7				4		
	8	9				2		
	3		9				4	7
	4		3	1				5
			7		4			

111 intermediate **04**

		1			9			2
	4		1	3			7	
	8	9						
1				7				
	3		8		1		5	
				6				3
						3	4	
	5			1	4		2	
9			5			8		

91

I have hardly ever known a mathematician
who was capable of reasoning.
Plato

112 intermediate **04**

			3			7		
	5	7			9		6	
4					8	1		
		4		5	6		9	
	7						4	
	9		4	3		2		
		2	9					4
	4		6			9	8	
		5			2			

113 intermediate 04

	3		2	1		8		
		4	3				6	
		8				1		3
2					4			
	8		5		7		1	
			8					6
7		1				6		
	5				6	9		
		3		8	2		7	

114 intermediate 04

6						9		
		3	4			5		8
	7			6	8			3
	1			4				
3		7				2		5
				1			3	
7			6	5			9	
8		2			3	6		
		4						7

115 intermediate 04

7						6		
1				6	8	5		
				7	9		2	3
	1	6			5		9	
	8		6			4	3	
6	3		2	9				
		2	7	1				4
		4						2

116 intermediate 04

		1	4				2	
				3				
3		9			8			6
		3		4				8
	6		3		9		1	
5				2		4		
6			9			8		4
				6				
	7				4	2		

A good calculator does not need artificial aids.
Lao Tze

6			9		7			
	3							9
				4		2	3	
2				7	4	6		
		6	5		9	1		
		7	6	8				2
	4	1		9				
8							7	
			7		5			4

97

The control of large numbers is possible, and like unto that of small numbers, if we subdivide them.
Sun Tze Ping Fa

118

intermediate

04

			2			9		
2	3		1					
		9		5			2	4
1				3	6	7		
			9		1			
		7	5	8				3
7	1			9		8		
					4		9	6
		4			5			

					2			5
		4	1					
	7						2	4
	2		4	3			8	
		7	8		5	4		
	9			1	7		6	
6	4						9	
					1	3		
9			6					

99

It is not enough to have a good mind.
The main thing is to use it well.
René Descartes

120 intermediate 04

		2		3		1		
		8	2	4				7
5					8		3	
2					4	6		8
4		7	6					1
	2		4					6
8				1	6	9		
		4		5		7		

							1	3
		5			9			
		9	1	3		2		
	1			5	4			9
		7	9		2	5		
5			7	1			3	
		1		6	3	8		
			4			1		
9	6							

101

121 intermediate

122 intermediate 04

			1	9		4	8	
			2					9
				6	7	1		3
					6	7		8
		7				2		
4		8	5					
6		1	8	5				
8					4			
	7	4		2	3			

123 intermediate

	8				6			
		6	1	2		7		
	2				9			
		4	5				9	8
3	6						1	4
5	9				1	2		
			9				4	
		2		1	5	9		
			8				3	

124 intermediate 04

7			5	6	4			
		5					7	
			2			1	4	
1		6						9
	3	7				5	1	
5						2		4
	1	2			3			
	5					4		
			8	2	6			1

104

... numbers have neither substance, nor meaning, nor qualities. They are nothing but marks, and all that is in them we have put into them by the simple rule of straight succession.

Hermann Weyl

125 intermediate 04

	4		5				2	9
		9	1					
	6			8			3	4
3				6				
		5	8		2	3		
				1				5
7	2			4			5	
					1	6		
9	5				3		8	

126 intermediate 04

				8			2	
	3	5	2					
		8		6	9			5
3					4			8
4		7				1		3
5			6					2
7			9	5		2		
					6	9	1	
	6			1				

		1	3					
	4					5		
5		9			8		2	
	3			4	6		8	
2								5
	9		5	7			3	
	1		9			3		7
		3					9	
					2	6		

107

Sudoku Addict Alert! Hi, I am Lucy and I'm a Sudoku addict!
Lucy

128 intermediate 04

4					7		5	6
	2		3					9
		8	2	5				
	1	6	7					
3								2
					1	4	7	
				6	2	8		
8					3		6	
9	6		8					1

	1		6				8	
2	5		1					7
		9		5	8			
1						7		
	8		9		1		3	
		7						4
			2	9		8		
8					3		5	1
	6				4		7	

109

The science of pure mathematics ... may claim to be the most original creation of the human spirit.
Alfred North Whitehead

130 intermediate 04

		1	2				9	
2			1					8
	6		4	7			2	
	2	3		4				
			9		6			
				2		4	5	
	1			9	3		4	
8					2			6
	5				4	3		

131 intermediate 04

	8					3	6	
			4					9
			3			1	2	5
2	1			3				
3			8		5			6
				2			7	3
6	3	1			2			
8					7			
	7	4					5	

		3	8					
	2	4			6			
5			1				4	6
2					5		7	
		7		9		1		
	8		6					5
6	3				2			7
			9			8	5	
					4	6		

112

It is here [in mathematics] that the artist has the
fullest scope of his imagination.
Havelock Ellis

133 intermediate 04

		4					3	
2				4	6			
	7				9	1		4
	2		4	3				8
4				2	1		6	
5		1	8				7	
			9	1				3
	9					4		

134 intermediate 04

				3		8	1	
	2		4		8			
5			1			2		
						7	9	
3			8		6			2
	8	9						
		1			4			7
			9		1		6	
	9	5		6				

		1	2	5				8
	3			4	8			9
			3					
1			4				9	7
	4						5	
5	8				2			3
					3			
7			8	1			6	
8				2	6	5		

115

135 intermediate 04

God does not care about our mathematical difficulties.
He integrates empirically.
Albert Einstein

136 intermediate 04

			5			3		
	3			7			6	8
5			3			1		
				2		7		9
4		7				6		1
6		8		3				
		1			2			3
8	5			1			7	
		3			4			

7	3	5	6					
	2	4		5				9
	8							
		6		3	5			
		7	2		9	1		
			7	1		3		
							8	
8				7		9	4	
					4	5	2	1

117

The latest authors, like the most ancient, strove to subordinate the phenomena of nature to the laws of mathematics.
Isaac Newton

138 intermediate 04

	9		3	6			2	
					7			
4				8		1		
			4		6	7		8
5		4				2		3
6		9	7		2			
		1		9				6
			6					
	5			2	4		7	

139 intermediate 04

3					1			9
	4						7	
5			4	6				
	1			4	6			7
	3		9		2		1	
6			1	7			3	
				9	4			6
	5						4	
9			8					1

140 intermediate 04

2	3		4	7				
		5			9			
		9				2	3	
				4				9
		6	7		1	3		
5				8				
	2	1				8		
			9			4		
				2	3		1	7

120

Of all things, good sense is the most fairly distributed: everyone thinks he is so well supplied with it that even those who are the hardest to satisfy in every other respect never desire more of it than they already have.

René Descartes

	6			8				7
1		5	3			6		
			1					5
2		3				7	9	
	8						2	
	9	7				5		3
7					4			
		2			5	9		1
9				2			7	

141 intermediate

04

142 intermediate 04

3						5		2
		4			6			9
	7				8			
2	1			7				
	8		6		3		1	
				8			5	3
			5				2	
8			7			9		
9		6						1

143 intermediate

04

					1	8		
1							7	
	8	9		5			2	
			6		5	7		
	6	7		8		2	5	
		8	1		7			
	4			9		3	8	
	5							6
		3	8					

144 intermediate 04

	1	6	4					
			1			5		8
	8		3	5	6			
1						6	8	
		7				4		
	9	8						7
			8	2	3		7	
8		2			7			
					5	8	1	

3					4	1	7	
		7		3	8	5		
							3	
2		3		4			9	
	9			1		4		3
	2							
		4	6	7		9		
	5	6	8					1

125

Music is the pleasure the human soul experiences from counting without being aware that it is counting.
Gottfried Wilhelm Leibniz

146 intermediate 04

	6	7		5				2
	4		1	2				9
					9		4	
2						7		
4			8		1			3
		9						4
	3		4					
7				1	3		8	
8				6		2	3	

147 intermediate 04

			9				8	3
	3			5				
6				4	7			
	1				5	7		
3		7				2		1
		8	7				5	
			8	9				4
				6			1	
9	6				4			

	9				7		8	
		6			8		7	
5			4	6				
2				4				8
4	3						5	6
6				7				1
				8	3			5
	5		6			9		
	6		7				3	

128

Though this be madness, yet there is method in't.
William Shakespeare

1								
2				4	7	6		
4		9			8	1		
					6			8
	8			1			7	
6			5					
		1	6			8		4
		3	7	5				2
								7

129

... mathematical proofs, like diamonds, are hard and clear, and will be touched with nothing but strict reasoning.

John Locke

150 intermediate 04

	5			7	8			
1			4					9
6	7		1				4	
		4		3	7			
			6	8		1		
	3				2		5	6
8					5			3
			8	1			2	

130

As yet a child, nor yet a fool to fame, I lisped in numbers,
for the numbers came.
Alexander Pope

05 expert

In this chapter you will:

- complete 26 expert-level Sudoku.

152

expert

05

					2			5
1					8		7	
	8						3	4
		6		4			9	8
		7	2		9	4		
4	9			1		3		
6	3						2	
	4		5					3
9			6					

			6	9	4	8		
2					8			
	8		2				3	
		5		4		7	9	
3								1
	9	8		1		6		
	3				5		8	
			9					7
		4	8	7	1			

132

Sudoku Addict Alert! Um, when I picked 'hard' I didn't realize.
Do you have a slightly easier puzzle?
Simon

154 expert 05

				8				
2	4				6	7		
6	7						2	3
1		6		4			9	
	8			6		2		7
5	1						6	4
		3	8				5	2
				2				

155 expert 05

		4			2	5		6
2				4			8	
	8		3					
	1				5		9	
4		7				3		5
	9		4				7	
					9		6	
	5			1				7
9		3	7			2		

156 expert 05

4			7					
				3				9
	7	9		5		1		
			3			5	9	8
3		6				4		7
5	9	7			2			
		2		4		8	6	
8				1				
					3			1

135

Sudoku Addict Alert! Not sure if this is a good thing or not, it is so addictive! I can always go to Sudoku anonymous later in life.
Meena

157 expert 05

	9				1			
	3	4		5	7			
5				8				3
2						5	9	
		8				2		
	7	9						6
6				4				5
			9	1		8	6	
			6				3	

		5			1			2
		4		5			8	
	7				8		3	
	1	6	4		7			
3								4
			5		2	3	1	
	4		8				7	
	6			1		8		
9			6			4		

137

If you would be a real seeker after truth, you must at least once in your life doubt, as far as possible, all things.

René Descartes

159 expert

05

		5			2	1	7	
1							8	
7				3	6			
	1				5	7		
3	5						1	6
		8	6				5	
			8	2				7
	6							4
	7	4	5			8		

160 expert 05

6	2			3		1		
		4			8			
7	8							4
	1		3	4		7		
			6		9			
		8		2	1		5	
5							2	6
			4			9		
		3		6			4	1

161 expert

05

					5			8
						6	7	
2	8	9		6				
	1	6	5		4			
		7	8		9	5		
			6		3	2	1	
				5		4	8	6
	5	2						
9			3					

162 expert 05

					5		6	3
					6	7	8	
3			1			2		5
2			4			6		
	7						5	
		9			1			7
6		1			2			4
	5	2	8					
8	9		6					

Like the crest of a peacock, so is mathematics at the
head of all knowledge.
Anonymous

163 expert

05

	2		8		9			
1		5						
					6		3	4
		6	3				9	8
3		7				4		2
4	9				2	3		
5	3		4					
						9		5
			6		5		1	

164 expert 05

				2				5
		5	1		8		7	
		8					2	3
1					5	7	9	
3								4
	9	7	4					1
6	4					9		
	5		9		7	3		
9				4				

		4						2
1	5					7		9
				7	8			
	1		5	4			9	
4								3
	9			2	6		7	
			4	8				
7		3					6	5
9						2		

144

An expert is a man who has made all the mistakes which can be made, in a very narrow field.
Niels Henrik David Bohr

			8	9				
		6	3			7	8	
						3	4	
	1		5			6		8
3								1
5		8			2		3	
	4	1						
	5	2			4	9		
				6	1			

145

The riddle does not exist. If a question can be put at all,
then it can also be answered.
Ludwig Wittgenstein

8					5		1	
	3					6		
2		9				3	4	
3					6			9
		6	8		2	1		
5			7					4
	2	1				8		7
		3					2	
	8		6					1

167 expert

05

168 expert 05

		8	3	9				6
1								9
	7		1					
2		4		3		6		
	8	6				5	7	
		7		8		4		3
					2		5	
8								7
9				7	4	1		

169 expert 05

5			1					
1	3		2			5		
6	7				8			
2					6		9	
	8						4	
	9		5					6
			9				6	2
		2			4		3	1
					1			7

I am ill at these numbers.
William Shakespeare

170 expert 05

9			4					
				2	5	7	8	
1						3	4	
				4		6		
		7	2		8	1		
		9		1				
	3	1						7
	5	2	8	3				
					2			3

171 expert 05

				9				
3		5			7			9
	7	9			8	1		
2			5		6			
		6				5		
			2		3			1
		1	9			8	4	
8			4			9		6
				7				

172

expert

05

		4		1			9	7
1	3			7	9			
		9			8			
	1	5						9
4								1
6						3	4	
			5			8		
			7	3			1	4
9	6			4		2		

			5	6		2	1	
	2		3					9
	7							
		6	4	3			9	
4			9		2			1
	8			1	6	4		
							5	
8					1		3	
	6	3		5	4			

173
expert

05

			3			5	7	
			1				6	9
		8			9	1		
3				4	6		9	
		6				3		
	9		2	8				4
		1	6			9		
8	5				7			
	6	4			5			

153

How can it be that mathematics, being after all a product of human thought independent of experience, is so admirably adapted to the objects of reality?

Albert Einstein

175 expert 05

4	2							3
	8	9	1					
5				8	9			
	3	4		6			7	
		5				3		
	9			3		2	4	
			5	4				8
					6	7	5	
9							3	1

176 expert

05

1		5					9	6
	4			2				
	8	9			6			
		3		4	5			9
				9				
5			3	7		2		
			7			9	5	
				1			4	
9	7					8		1

177 expert 05

7				4				5
	3		2				7	9
			3					
2	1			3		7		
		6	7		5	4		
		7		1			3	6
					3			
8	5				7		4	
9				8				1

Order is Heaven's first law.
Alexander Pope

09 solutions

In this chapter you will:

- **find the solutions to all the Sudoku in this book.**

Solution 1

4	5	8	2	9	3	6	1	7
1	2	3	4	6	7	5	8	9
6	7	9	1	5	8	2	3	4
2	1	4	5	3	6	7	9	8
3	8	6	9	7	1	4	5	2
5	9	7	8	2	4	1	6	3
7	3	1	6	4	9	8	2	5
8	4	2	3	1	5	9	7	6
9	6	5	7	8	2	3	4	1

Solution 2

5	8	2	1	4	3	6	9	7
1	3	6	2	7	9	4	5	8
4	7	9	5	6	8	1	2	3
2	1	5	4	3	6	7	8	9
3	4	7	9	8	1	2	6	5
6	9	8	7	5	2	3	1	4
7	2	1	3	9	5	8	4	6
8	5	3	6	1	4	9	7	2
9	6	4	8	2	7	5	3	1

Solution 3

5	4	3	7	6	2	9	8	1
1	2	8	3	4	9	5	6	7
6	7	9	1	5	8	2	3	4
2	1	5	4	3	6	8	7	9
3	8	6	9	7	5	1	4	2
4	9	7	2	8	1	3	5	6
7	3	1	8	2	4	6	9	5
8	5	2	6	9	7	4	1	3
9	6	4	5	1	3	7	2	8

Solution 4

2	7	1	6	5	8	3	4	9
3	4	5	1	2	9	6	7	8
6	8	9	3	4	7	1	2	5
1	2	6	4	3	5	8	9	7
4	3	7	9	8	1	5	6	2
5	9	8	2	7	6	4	3	1
7	1	2	5	6	3	9	8	4
8	5	3	7	9	4	2	1	6
9	6	4	8	1	2	7	5	3

Solution 5

7	3	6	4	5	2	1	8	9
1	2	4	3	8	9	5	6	7
5	8	9	1	6	7	2	3	4
2	1	5	6	3	4	7	9	8
3	6	7	9	2	8	4	1	5
4	9	8	5	7	1	6	2	3
6	4	1	8	9	5	3	7	2
8	5	2	7	1	3	9	4	6
9	7	3	2	4	6	8	5	1

Solution 6

1	6	4	7	5	3	2	8	9
2	3	8	1	4	9	5	6	7
5	7	9	2	6	8	1	3	4
3	1	2	4	7	5	6	9	8
4	8	5	6	9	1	3	7	2
6	9	7	3	8	2	4	5	1
7	2	1	9	3	6	8	4	5
8	4	3	5	1	7	9	2	6
9	5	6	8	2	4	7	1	3

Solution 7

1	9	3	8	4	5	2	6	7
2	4	6	1	3	7	5	8	9
5	7	8	2	6	9	1	3	4
3	1	5	4	2	6	7	9	8
4	2	7	3	9	8	6	5	1
6	8	9	5	7	1	3	4	2
7	3	1	6	8	4	9	2	5
8	5	2	9	1	3	4	7	6
9	6	4	7	5	2	8	1	3

Solution 8

4	5	2	7	9	8	3	6	1
1	3	6	2	4	5	7	8	9
7	8	9	1	3	6	2	4	5
2	1	4	3	5	7	6	9	8
3	6	7	9	8	1	5	2	4
5	9	8	6	2	4	1	3	7
6	2	1	4	7	9	8	5	3
8	4	3	5	1	2	9	7	6
9	7	5	8	6	3	4	1	2

Solution 9

3	1	2	9	4	6	7	8	5
5	7	8	1	2	3	4	6	9
4	6	9	5	7	8	1	2	3
1	3	4	2	5	7	6	9	8
2	8	5	4	6	9	3	1	7
6	9	7	3	8	1	2	5	4
7	2	1	8	9	4	5	3	6
8	4	3	6	1	5	9	7	2
9	5	6	7	3	2	8	4	1

Solution 10

7	4	9	8	2	1	6	5	3
1	2	3	4	5	6	7	8	9
5	6	8	3	7	9	1	2	4
2	1	5	6	3	7	4	9	8
3	8	6	2	9	4	5	1	7
4	9	7	1	8	5	3	6	2
6	3	1	9	4	2	8	7	5
8	5	2	7	1	3	9	4	6
9	7	4	5	6	8	2	3	1

Solution 11

5	2	9	7	1	4	3	8	6
1	3	4	2	6	8	5	7	9
6	7	8	3	5	9	1	2	4
2	1	5	4	3	6	7	9	8
3	8	6	5	9	7	2	4	1
4	9	7	1	8	2	6	5	3
7	4	1	9	2	3	8	6	5
8	5	2	6	4	1	9	3	7
9	6	3	8	7	5	4	1	2

Solution 12

6	3	8	5	1	9	4	7	2
1	2	5	3	4	7	6	8	9
4	7	9	2	6	8	1	3	5
2	1	4	6	3	5	7	9	8
3	8	6	7	9	1	2	5	4
5	9	7	8	2	4	3	6	1
7	4	1	9	5	3	8	2	6
8	5	2	1	7	6	9	4	3
9	6	3	4	8	2	5	1	7

Solution 13

5	9	3	4	2	1	6	8	7
1	2	6	3	7	8	4	5	9
4	7	8	5	6	9	1	2	3
2	1	5	6	3	4	7	9	8
3	4	7	8	9	2	5	1	6
6	8	9	1	5	7	3	4	2
7	3	1	9	8	5	2	6	4
8	5	2	7	4	6	9	3	1
9	6	4	2	1	3	8	7	5

Solution 14

6	7	8	5	1	3	4	2	9
1	3	5	2	4	9	6	7	8
2	4	9	6	7	8	1	3	5
3	1	2	4	5	6	8	9	7
4	8	6	3	9	7	2	5	1
5	9	7	1	8	2	3	4	6
7	2	1	9	6	4	5	8	3
8	5	3	7	2	1	9	6	4
9	6	4	8	3	5	7	1	2

Solution 15

7	2	5	8	3	4	1	9	6
1	3	4	2	6	9	5	7	8
6	8	9	1	5	7	2	3	4
2	1	6	3	4	5	7	8	9
3	5	7	6	9	8	4	1	2
4	9	8	7	1	2	3	6	5
5	4	1	9	8	3	6	2	7
8	6	2	4	7	1	9	5	3
9	7	3	5	2	6	8	4	1

Solution 16

5	2	7	9	8	4	6	3	1
1	3	4	2	5	6	7	8	9
6	8	9	1	3	7	2	4	5
2	1	5	6	7	3	4	9	8
3	7	6	8	4	9	1	5	2
4	9	8	5	1	2	3	6	7
7	4	1	3	9	5	8	2	6
8	5	2	4	6	1	9	7	3
9	6	3	7	2	8	5	1	4

Solution 17

3	2	5	4	8	7	6	1	9
1	4	6	2	3	9	5	7	8
7	8	9	1	5	6	2	3	4
2	1	3	6	4	5	8	9	7
4	6	7	9	2	8	1	5	3
5	9	8	3	7	1	4	2	6
6	3	1	5	9	4	7	8	2
8	5	2	7	6	3	9	4	1
9	7	4	8	1	2	3	6	5

Solution 18

4	6	1	8	5	3	2	9	7
2	3	7	1	4	9	5	6	8
5	8	9	2	6	7	1	3	4
1	2	4	5	3	6	7	8	9
3	7	5	9	8	2	6	4	1
6	9	8	4	7	1	3	2	5
7	1	2	3	9	8	4	5	6
8	4	3	6	1	5	9	7	2
9	5	6	7	2	4	8	1	3

Solution 19

9	5	4	6	2	3	8	7	1
1	2	3	4	7	8	5	6	9
6	7	8	1	5	9	2	3	4
2	1	5	3	4	6	7	9	8
3	6	7	9	8	2	1	4	5
4	8	9	5	1	7	3	2	6
5	3	1	2	6	4	9	8	7
7	4	2	8	9	1	6	5	3
8	9	6	7	3	5	4	1	2

Solution 20

8	1	5	4	2	7	9	3	6
2	3	4	1	6	9	5	7	8
6	7	9	3	5	8	1	2	4
1	2	6	5	3	4	7	8	9
3	5	7	8	9	6	4	1	2
4	9	8	2	7	1	6	5	3
5	4	1	6	8	2	3	9	7
7	6	2	9	1	3	8	4	5
9	8	3	7	4	5	2	6	1

Solution 21

6	8	3	2	9	1	4	5	7
1	2	4	3	5	7	6	8	9
5	7	9	4	6	8	1	2	3
2	1	6	5	3	4	7	9	8
3	5	7	8	1	9	2	6	4
4	9	8	7	2	6	3	1	5
7	3	1	9	8	2	5	4	6
8	4	2	6	7	5	9	3	1
9	6	5	1	4	3	8	7	2

Solution 22

1	5	6	3	8	9	7	2	4
2	3	4	1	5	7	6	8	9
7	8	9	2	4	6	1	3	5
3	1	2	6	7	5	4	9	8
4	6	7	9	2	8	5	1	3
5	9	8	4	3	1	2	7	6
6	2	1	5	9	3	8	4	7
8	4	3	7	6	2	9	5	1
9	7	5	8	1	4	3	6	2

Solution 23

3	4	7	9	6	8	2	1	5
1	2	6	3	4	5	7	8	9
5	8	9	1	2	7	3	4	6
2	1	3	5	7	4	6	9	8
4	7	5	8	9	6	1	2	3
6	9	8	2	3	1	4	5	7
7	3	1	4	5	9	8	6	2
8	5	2	6	1	3	9	7	4
9	6	4	7	8	2	5	3	1

Solution 24

4	7	1	9	8	6	2	5	3
2	3	6	1	4	5	7	8	9
5	8	9	2	3	7	1	4	6
1	2	5	3	7	4	6	9	8
3	4	7	8	6	9	5	1	2
6	9	8	5	1	2	4	3	7
7	1	2	4	9	3	8	6	5
8	5	3	6	2	1	9	7	4
9	6	4	7	5	8	3	2	1

Solution 25

4	3	6	5	9	2	7	1	8
1	2	7	3	4	8	5	6	9
5	8	9	1	6	7	2	3	4
2	1	4	6	3	5	8	9	7
3	7	5	2	8	9	6	4	1
6	9	8	4	7	1	3	5	2
7	4	1	8	5	3	9	2	6
8	5	2	9	1	6	4	7	3
9	6	3	7	2	4	1	8	5

Solution 26

2	3	9	5	4	8	1	6	7
1	4	6	2	3	7	5	8	9
5	7	8	1	6	9	2	3	4
3	1	2	4	5	6	7	9	8
4	8	5	9	7	2	6	1	3
6	9	7	3	8	1	4	5	2
7	2	1	6	9	3	8	4	5
8	5	3	7	1	4	9	2	6
9	6	4	8	2	5	3	7	1

Solution 27

6	3	4	5	2	1	9	7	8
1	2	7	3	8	9	4	5	6
5	8	9	4	6	7	1	2	3
2	1	5	6	3	4	7	8	9
3	7	6	9	5	8	2	1	4
4	9	8	7	1	2	6	3	5
7	4	1	8	9	3	5	6	2
8	5	2	1	4	6	3	9	7
9	6	3	2	7	5	8	4	1

Solution 28

3	9	6	2	7	5	1	8	4
1	2	5	3	4	8	6	7	9
4	7	8	1	6	9	2	3	5
2	1	4	5	3	6	7	9	8
5	3	7	9	8	1	4	2	6
6	8	9	4	2	7	3	5	1
7	4	1	8	9	2	5	6	3
8	5	2	6	1	3	9	4	7
9	6	3	7	5	4	8	1	2

Solution 29

9	2	3	5	8	7	6	4	1
1	4	5	2	3	6	7	8	9
6	7	8	1	4	9	2	3	5
2	1	6	3	7	4	5	9	8
3	5	7	8	9	1	4	2	6
4	8	9	6	5	2	1	7	3
5	3	1	4	2	8	9	6	7
7	6	2	9	1	3	8	5	4
8	9	4	7	6	5	3	1	2

Solution 30

3	9	4	8	2	7	1	5	6
1	2	5	3	4	6	7	8	9
6	7	8	1	5	9	2	3	4
2	1	6	7	3	4	5	9	8
4	3	7	9	8	5	6	2	1
5	8	9	6	1	2	4	7	3
7	4	1	2	9	8	3	6	5
8	5	2	4	6	3	9	1	7
9	6	3	5	7	1	8	4	2

Solution 31

1	7	2	9	6	4	8	5	3
3	4	5	1	2	8	6	7	9
6	8	9	3	5	7	1	2	4
2	1	6	4	3	5	7	9	8
4	3	7	2	8	9	5	6	1
5	9	8	7	1	6	3	4	2
7	2	1	5	4	3	9	8	6
8	5	3	6	9	2	4	1	7
9	6	4	8	7	1	2	3	5

Solution 32

5	2	6	9	4	7	3	8	1
1	3	4	2	5	8	6	7	9
7	8	9	1	3	6	2	4	5
2	1	5	3	6	4	7	9	8
3	6	7	5	8	9	4	1	2
4	9	8	7	2	1	5	3	6
6	4	1	8	7	2	9	5	3
8	5	2	4	9	3	1	6	7
9	7	3	6	1	5	8	2	4

Solution 33

8	1	3	2	5	6	9	7	4
2	4	7	1	3	9	5	6	8
5	6	9	4	7	8	1	2	3
1	2	5	3	6	4	7	8	9
3	7	6	8	9	2	4	1	5
4	9	8	5	1	7	6	3	2
6	3	1	9	8	5	2	4	7
7	5	2	6	4	3	8	9	1
9	8	4	7	2	1	3	5	6

Solution 34

6	4	7	8	5	3	1	9	2
1	3	5	2	4	9	6	7	8
2	8	9	1	6	7	3	4	5
3	1	2	4	7	6	5	8	9
4	7	6	5	9	8	2	1	3
5	9	8	3	2	1	4	6	7
7	2	1	6	8	5	9	3	4
8	5	3	9	1	4	7	2	6
9	6	4	7	3	2	8	5	1

Solution 35

6	9	1	3	4	2	7	5	8
2	3	5	1	7	8	4	6	9
4	7	8	5	6	9	1	2	3
1	2	6	4	3	5	8	9	7
3	4	7	8	9	6	2	1	5
5	8	9	2	1	7	3	4	6
7	1	2	6	5	3	9	8	4
8	5	3	9	2	4	6	7	1
9	6	4	7	8	1	5	3	2

Solution 36

4	9	2	3	6	5	8	7	1
1	3	7	2	4	8	5	6	9
5	6	8	1	7	9	2	3	4
2	1	4	5	3	6	7	9	8
3	7	5	9	8	1	6	4	2
6	8	9	4	2	7	1	5	3
7	2	1	6	9	3	4	8	5
8	4	3	7	5	2	9	1	6
9	5	6	8	1	4	3	2	7

Solution 37

6	7	8	1	4	9	2	3	5
1	2	4	3	5	6	7	8	9
3	5	9	2	7	8	1	4	6
2	1	3	4	6	7	5	9	8
4	8	6	5	9	1	3	2	7
5	9	7	8	2	3	4	6	1
7	3	1	6	8	2	9	5	4
8	4	2	9	1	5	6	7	3
9	6	5	7	3	4	8	1	2

Solution 38

7	3	5	9	1	4	2	6	8
1	2	4	3	6	8	5	7	9
6	8	9	2	5	7	1	3	4
2	1	6	4	3	5	8	9	7
3	5	7	8	9	6	4	2	1
4	9	8	1	7	2	3	5	6
5	4	1	6	2	9	7	8	3
8	6	2	7	4	3	9	1	5
9	7	3	5	8	1	6	4	2

Solution 39

9	7	6	4	2	1	8	3	5
1	2	4	3	5	8	6	7	9
3	5	8	6	7	9	1	2	4
2	1	3	5	4	6	7	9	8
4	6	7	9	8	3	2	5	1
5	8	9	2	1	7	4	6	3
6	3	1	8	9	2	5	4	7
7	4	2	1	3	5	9	8	6
8	9	5	7	6	4	3	1	2

Solution 40

1	6	5	3	8	4	7	2	9
2	3	4	1	7	9	5	6	8
7	8	9	2	5	6	1	3	4
3	1	6	4	2	5	8	9	7
4	2	7	6	9	8	3	1	5
5	9	8	7	1	3	2	4	6
6	4	1	5	3	7	9	8	2
8	5	2	9	4	1	6	7	3
9	7	3	8	6	2	4	5	1

Solution 41

5	4	9	7	6	3	2	8	1
1	2	3	4	5	8	6	7	9
6	7	8	1	2	9	3	4	5
2	1	5	3	4	6	7	9	8
3	8	6	9	1	7	4	5	2
4	9	7	2	8	5	1	3	6
7	3	1	5	9	2	8	6	4
8	5	2	6	3	4	9	1	7
9	6	4	8	7	1	5	2	3

Solution 42

9	1	4	8	6	5	3	2	7
2	3	5	1	4	7	6	8	9
6	7	8	2	3	9	1	4	5
1	2	6	3	5	4	7	9	8
3	5	7	6	9	8	2	1	4
4	8	9	7	1	2	5	3	6
5	4	1	9	7	3	8	6	2
7	6	2	4	8	1	9	5	3
8	9	3	5	2	6	4	7	1

Solution 43

1	5	9	2	6	8	3	4	7
2	3	4	1	5	7	6	8	9
6	7	8	3	4	9	1	2	5
3	1	2	4	7	6	5	9	8
4	8	6	5	9	1	2	7	3
5	9	7	8	3	2	4	1	6
7	2	1	6	8	3	9	5	4
8	4	3	9	1	5	7	6	2
9	6	5	7	2	4	8	3	1

Solution 44

4	3	2	8	6	9	5	7	1
1	5	7	2	3	4	6	8	9
6	8	9	1	5	7	2	3	4
2	1	4	5	7	6	3	9	8
3	7	6	4	9	8	1	5	2
5	9	8	3	1	2	4	6	7
7	2	1	6	8	3	9	4	5
8	4	3	9	2	5	7	1	6
9	6	5	7	4	1	8	2	3

Solution 45

8	4	3	5	9	7	2	1	6
1	2	5	3	4	6	7	8	9
6	7	9	1	2	8	3	4	5
2	1	6	7	3	4	5	9	8
3	5	7	9	8	1	4	6	2
4	9	8	6	5	2	1	7	3
5	3	1	4	6	9	8	2	7
7	6	2	8	1	3	9	5	4
9	8	4	2	7	5	6	3	1

Solution 46

6	3	5	9	1	8	4	2	7
1	2	4	3	5	7	6	8	9
7	8	9	2	4	6	1	3	5
2	1	6	4	3	5	7	9	8
3	5	7	6	8	9	2	4	1
4	9	8	7	2	1	5	6	3
5	4	1	8	9	2	3	7	6
8	6	2	1	7	3	9	5	4
9	7	3	5	6	4	8	1	2

Solution 47

8	3	7	1	9	2	6	4	5
1	2	4	3	5	6	7	8	9
5	6	9	4	7	8	1	2	3
2	1	5	6	3	7	4	9	8
3	7	6	9	8	4	2	5	1
4	9	8	2	1	5	3	7	6
6	4	1	5	2	9	8	3	7
7	5	2	8	6	3	9	1	4
9	8	3	7	4	1	5	6	2

Solution 48

7	4	8	3	9	6	1	2	5
1	3	6	2	4	5	7	8	9
2	5	9	1	7	8	3	4	6
3	6	1	4	2	7	5	9	8
4	8	2	5	1	9	6	3	7
5	9	7	6	8	3	4	1	2
6	1	3	9	5	2	8	7	4
8	2	4	7	6	1	9	5	3
9	7	5	8	3	4	2	6	1

Solution 49

7	5	4	1	2	9	3	8	6
1	2	3	4	6	8	5	7	9
6	8	9	3	5	7	1	2	4
2	1	5	6	3	4	7	9	8
3	6	7	9	8	1	4	5	2
4	9	8	5	7	2	6	1	3
5	3	1	2	9	6	8	4	7
8	4	2	7	1	3	9	6	5
9	7	6	8	4	5	2	3	1

Solution 50

5	3	4	7	8	1	2	9	6
1	2	6	3	4	9	5	7	8
7	8	9	2	5	6	1	3	4
2	1	5	6	3	4	7	8	9
3	6	7	8	9	5	4	1	2
4	9	8	1	2	7	6	5	3
6	4	1	9	7	8	3	2	5
8	5	2	4	1	3	9	6	7
9	7	3	5	6	2	8	4	1

Solution 51

1	6	9	3	8	7	5	2	4
2	3	4	1	5	6	7	8	9
5	7	8	2	4	9	1	3	6
3	1	2	4	7	5	6	9	8
4	8	5	9	6	2	3	1	7
6	9	7	8	1	3	4	5	2
7	2	1	5	9	4	8	6	3
8	4	3	6	2	1	9	7	5
9	5	6	7	3	8	2	4	1

Solution 52

9	6	7	2	1	3	5	4	8
1	2	3	4	5	8	6	7	9
4	5	8	6	7	9	1	2	3
2	1	4	5	3	6	8	9	7
3	7	6	8	9	4	2	5	1
5	8	9	1	2	7	3	6	4
6	3	1	9	4	2	7	8	5
7	4	2	3	8	5	9	1	6
8	9	5	7	6	1	4	3	2

Solution 53

1	2	9	5	8	7	6	3	4
3	4	5	1	2	6	7	8	9
6	7	8	3	4	9	1	2	5
2	1	3	6	7	4	5	9	8
4	8	6	9	3	5	2	1	7
5	9	7	2	1	8	4	6	3
7	3	1	4	9	2	8	5	6
8	5	2	7	6	3	9	4	1
9	6	4	8	5	1	3	7	2

Solution 54

1	7	6	2	5	3	8	9	4
2	3	4	1	8	9	5	6	7
5	8	9	4	6	7	1	2	3
3	1	5	6	2	4	7	8	9
4	2	7	9	3	8	6	1	5
6	9	8	7	1	5	3	4	2
7	4	1	5	9	6	2	3	8
8	5	2	3	4	1	9	7	6
9	6	3	8	7	2	4	5	1

Solution 55

7	3	1	4	5	9	8	2	6
2	4	6	1	3	8	5	7	9
5	8	9	2	6	7	1	3	4
1	2	5	3	4	6	7	9	8
3	6	7	9	8	1	2	4	5
4	9	8	5	7	2	3	6	1
6	1	2	7	9	5	4	8	3
8	5	3	6	2	4	9	1	7
9	7	4	8	1	3	6	5	2

Solution 56

3	5	7	9	2	1	4	8	6
1	2	4	3	6	8	5	7	9
6	8	9	4	5	7	1	2	3
2	1	3	5	4	6	7	9	8
4	7	6	1	8	9	2	3	5
5	9	8	2	7	3	6	1	4
7	3	1	6	9	4	8	5	2
8	4	2	7	3	5	9	6	1
9	6	5	8	1	2	3	4	7

Solution 57

2	4	5	3	8	6	9	7	1
1	3	7	2	4	9	5	6	8
6	8	9	1	5	7	2	3	4
3	1	2	4	6	5	7	8	9
4	7	6	9	2	8	1	5	3
5	9	8	7	1	3	6	4	2
7	2	1	5	3	4	8	9	6
8	5	3	6	9	1	4	2	7
9	6	4	8	7	2	3	1	5

Solution 58

5	9	1	3	4	2	6	7	8
2	3	6	1	7	8	4	5	9
4	7	8	5	6	9	1	2	3
1	2	5	4	3	6	8	9	7
3	4	7	9	8	5	2	6	1
6	8	9	2	1	7	5	3	4
7	1	2	6	9	4	3	8	5
8	5	3	7	2	1	9	4	6
9	6	4	8	5	3	7	1	2

Solution 59

9	4	3	1	7	6	5	8	2
1	2	5	3	4	8	6	7	9
6	7	8	2	5	9	1	3	4
2	1	6	4	3	5	7	9	8
3	5	7	8	9	2	4	1	6
4	8	9	7	6	1	2	5	3
5	3	1	9	2	4	8	6	7
7	6	2	5	8	3	9	4	1
8	9	4	6	1	7	3	2	5

Solution 60

6	1	7	9	4	2	5	3	8
2	3	4	1	5	8	6	7	9
5	8	9	3	6	7	1	2	4
1	2	5	4	3	6	8	9	7
3	7	6	2	8	9	4	1	5
4	9	8	5	7	1	3	6	2
7	4	1	6	9	5	2	8	3
8	5	2	7	1	3	9	4	6
9	6	3	8	2	4	7	5	1

Solution 61

5	1	8	7	4	9	2	3	6
2	3	4	1	5	6	7	8	9
6	7	9	2	3	8	1	4	5
1	2	5	3	7	4	6	9	8
3	8	6	5	9	2	4	1	7
4	9	7	6	8	1	3	5	2
7	4	1	9	2	5	8	6	3
8	5	2	4	6	3	9	7	1
9	6	3	8	1	7	5	2	4

Solution 62

5	4	9	6	7	2	1	3	8
1	2	3	4	5	8	6	7	9
6	7	8	1	3	9	2	4	5
2	1	5	3	4	6	8	9	7
3	8	6	9	2	7	4	5	1
4	9	7	5	8	1	3	6	2
7	3	1	2	9	4	5	8	6
8	5	2	7	6	3	9	1	4
9	6	4	8	1	5	7	2	3

Solution 63

7	4	5	3	8	1	6	9	2
1	2	3	4	6	9	5	7	8
6	8	9	2	5	7	1	3	4
2	1	6	5	3	4	7	8	9
3	5	7	9	1	8	2	4	6
4	9	8	6	7	2	3	1	5
5	3	1	8	9	6	4	2	7
8	6	2	7	4	3	9	5	1
9	7	4	1	2	5	8	6	3

Solution 64

3	5	4	8	2	6	9	7	1
1	2	7	3	4	9	5	6	8
6	8	9	1	5	7	2	3	4
2	1	3	4	6	5	7	8	9
4	7	6	9	1	8	3	5	2
5	9	8	2	7	3	1	4	6
7	3	1	6	9	4	8	2	5
8	4	2	5	3	1	6	9	7
9	6	5	7	8	2	4	1	3

Solution 65

9	2	8	5	1	4	3	6	7
1	3	4	2	6	7	5	8	9
5	6	7	3	8	9	1	2	4
2	1	5	4	3	6	7	9	8
3	7	6	8	9	2	4	5	1
4	8	9	1	7	5	2	3	6
6	4	1	9	2	3	8	7	5
7	5	2	6	4	8	9	1	3
8	9	3	7	5	1	6	4	2

Solution 66

1	3	2	6	4	8	9	5	7
5	7	9	1	2	3	4	6	8
4	6	8	5	7	9	1	2	3
2	1	4	3	5	6	7	8	9
3	8	5	2	9	7	6	1	4
6	9	7	8	1	4	2	3	5
7	2	1	4	3	5	8	9	6
8	4	3	9	6	1	5	7	2
9	5	6	7	8	2	3	4	1

Solution 67

9	4	7	5	6	2	1	3	8
1	2	5	3	4	8	6	7	9
3	6	8	1	7	9	2	4	5
2	1	3	4	5	6	8	9	7
4	7	6	8	9	1	3	5	2
5	8	9	2	3	7	4	1	6
6	3	1	9	8	5	7	2	4
7	5	2	6	1	4	9	8	3
8	9	4	7	2	3	5	6	1

Solution 68

7	4	9	8	3	2	6	1	5
1	2	3	4	5	6	7	8	9
5	6	8	1	7	9	2	3	4
2	1	5	3	6	7	4	9	8
3	8	6	2	9	4	5	7	1
4	9	7	5	1	8	3	2	6
6	3	1	7	8	5	9	4	2
8	5	2	9	4	3	1	6	7
9	7	4	6	2	1	8	5	3

Solution 69

6	7	5	1	4	3	8	9	2
1	3	4	2	8	9	5	6	7
2	8	9	5	6	7	1	3	4
3	1	6	4	2	5	7	8	9
4	2	7	8	9	6	3	1	5
5	9	8	3	7	1	2	4	6
7	4	1	9	3	2	6	5	8
8	5	2	6	1	4	9	7	3
9	6	3	7	5	8	4	2	1

Solution 70

5	3	2	8	7	1	6	4	9
1	4	6	2	3	9	5	7	8
7	8	9	4	5	6	1	2	3
2	1	5	3	6	4	8	9	7
3	6	7	9	2	8	4	5	1
4	9	8	5	1	7	2	3	6
6	2	1	7	4	3	9	8	5
8	5	3	1	9	2	7	6	4
9	7	4	6	8	5	3	1	2

Solution 71

9	6	7	5	8	3	4	2	1
1	3	5	2	4	6	7	8	9
2	4	8	1	7	9	3	5	6
3	1	2	4	5	7	6	9	8
4	7	6	9	2	8	1	3	5
5	8	9	3	6	1	2	4	7
6	2	1	8	3	5	9	7	4
7	5	3	6	9	4	8	1	2
8	9	4	7	1	2	5	6	3

Solution 72

3	4	8	6	7	5	9	2	1
1	2	5	3	4	9	6	7	8
6	7	9	1	2	8	3	4	5
2	1	3	4	5	6	7	8	9
4	8	6	7	9	1	2	5	3
5	9	7	2	8	3	4	1	6
7	3	1	5	6	2	8	9	4
8	5	2	9	3	4	1	6	7
9	6	4	8	1	7	5	3	2

Solution 73

6	8	3	1	5	2	9	7	4
1	2	4	3	7	9	5	6	8
5	7	9	4	6	8	1	2	3
2	1	6	5	3	4	7	8	9
3	5	7	8	9	1	2	4	6
4	9	8	6	2	7	3	5	1
7	3	1	2	8	6	4	9	5
8	4	2	9	1	5	6	3	7
9	6	5	7	4	3	8	1	2

Solution 74

4	2	5	9	7	8	1	6	3
1	3	6	2	4	5	7	8	9
7	8	9	1	3	6	2	4	5
2	1	4	3	5	7	6	9	8
3	6	7	4	8	9	5	1	2
5	9	8	6	1	2	3	7	4
6	4	1	5	9	3	8	2	7
8	5	2	7	6	4	9	3	1
9	7	3	8	2	1	4	5	6

Solution 75

7	9	1	6	3	2	8	4	5
2	3	4	1	5	8	6	7	9
5	6	8	4	7	9	1	2	3
1	2	6	3	4	5	7	9	8
3	5	7	9	8	1	2	6	4
4	8	9	2	6	7	5	3	1
6	1	2	5	9	3	4	8	7
8	4	3	7	1	6	9	5	2
9	7	5	8	2	4	3	1	6

Solution 76

1	5	7	6	3	2	8	9	4
2	3	4	1	8	9	5	6	7
6	8	9	4	5	7	1	2	3
3	1	2	5	4	6	7	8	9
4	7	6	2	9	8	3	1	5
5	9	8	7	1	3	2	4	6
7	2	1	3	6	4	9	5	8
8	4	3	9	2	5	6	7	1
9	6	5	8	7	1	4	3	2

Solution 77

4	7	9	5	8	1	6	2	3
1	2	5	3	4	6	7	8	9
3	6	8	2	7	9	1	4	5
2	1	3	4	6	7	5	9	8
5	8	4	1	9	3	2	6	7
6	9	7	8	5	2	4	3	1
7	3	1	6	2	8	9	5	4
8	4	2	9	1	5	3	7	6
9	5	6	7	3	4	8	1	2

Solution 78

2	7	9	4	6	8	5	3	1
1	4	6	2	3	5	7	8	9
3	5	8	1	7	9	2	4	6
4	1	2	3	5	7	6	9	8
5	8	3	6	9	2	4	1	7
6	9	7	8	1	4	3	5	2
7	2	1	5	8	3	9	6	4
8	3	4	9	2	6	1	7	5
9	6	5	7	4	1	8	2	3

Solution 79

8	6	5	4	9	7	2	3	1
1	2	4	3	5	6	7	8	9
3	7	9	1	2	8	4	5	6
2	1	6	7	3	4	5	9	8
4	3	7	5	8	9	6	1	2
5	9	8	6	1	2	3	4	7
6	4	1	8	7	3	9	2	5
7	5	2	9	4	1	8	6	3
9	8	3	2	6	5	1	7	4

Solution 80

1	2	7	9	4	3	6	8	5
3	5	6	1	2	8	4	7	9
4	8	9	5	6	7	1	2	3
2	1	3	4	5	6	7	9	8
5	7	4	3	8	9	2	6	1
6	9	8	7	1	2	5	3	4
7	3	1	2	9	4	8	5	6
8	4	2	6	3	5	9	1	7
9	6	5	8	7	1	3	4	2

Solution 81

4	8	1	9	5	7	2	6	3
2	3	5	1	4	6	7	8	9
6	7	9	2	3	8	1	4	5
1	2	6	3	7	4	5	9	8
3	4	7	5	8	9	6	1	2
5	9	8	6	1	2	4	3	7
7	1	2	4	9	3	8	5	6
8	5	3	7	6	1	9	2	4
9	6	4	8	2	5	3	7	1

Solution 82

4	9	6	7	1	5	2	8	3
1	2	5	3	4	8	6	7	9
3	7	8	2	6	9	1	4	5
2	1	4	5	3	6	7	9	8
5	3	7	8	9	1	4	6	2
6	8	9	4	2	7	3	5	1
7	4	1	9	8	2	5	3	6
8	5	2	6	7	3	9	1	4
9	6	3	1	5	4	8	2	7

Solution 83

3	5	2	9	6	8	7	1	4
1	4	7	2	3	5	6	8	9
6	8	9	1	4	7	2	3	5
2	1	3	4	7	6	5	9	8
4	7	6	5	8	9	3	2	1
5	9	8	3	1	2	4	7	6
7	2	1	6	9	4	8	5	3
8	3	4	7	5	1	9	6	2
9	6	5	8	2	3	1	4	7

Solution 84

4	5	8	9	3	6	2	7	1
1	2	3	4	5	7	6	8	9
6	7	9	1	2	8	3	4	5
2	1	4	3	6	5	7	9	8
3	8	6	7	9	1	5	2	4
5	9	7	2	8	4	1	3	6
7	3	1	5	4	9	8	6	2
8	4	2	6	1	3	9	5	7
9	6	5	8	7	2	4	1	3

Solution 85

7	9	2	3	8	5	4	6	1
1	3	5	2	4	6	7	8	9
4	6	8	1	7	9	2	3	5
2	1	6	4	3	7	5	9	8
3	4	7	5	9	8	1	2	6
5	8	9	6	1	2	3	7	4
6	2	1	9	5	3	8	4	7
8	5	3	7	6	4	9	1	2
9	7	4	8	2	1	6	5	3

Solution 86

8	1	6	5	9	2	4	7	3
2	3	5	1	4	7	6	8	9
4	7	9	3	6	8	1	2	5
1	2	4	6	3	5	7	9	8
3	6	7	9	8	1	2	5	4
5	9	8	2	7	4	3	6	1
6	4	1	7	5	9	8	3	2
7	5	2	8	1	3	9	4	6
9	8	3	4	2	6	5	1	7

Solution 87

7	9	8	3	1	2	6	4	5
1	2	3	4	5	6	7	8	9
4	5	6	7	8	9	1	2	3
2	1	4	6	3	7	5	9	8
3	6	7	5	9	8	2	1	4
5	8	9	2	4	1	3	7	6
6	3	1	9	7	4	8	5	2
8	4	2	1	6	5	9	3	7
9	7	5	8	2	3	4	6	1

Solution 88

8	3	2	1	4	7	6	9	5
1	5	6	2	3	9	4	7	8
4	7	9	5	6	8	1	2	3
2	1	4	3	5	6	7	8	9
3	6	7	8	9	2	5	4	1
5	9	8	4	7	1	2	3	6
6	2	1	7	8	3	9	5	4
7	4	3	9	1	5	8	6	2
9	8	5	6	2	4	3	1	7

Solution 89

7	6	9	1	3	2	8	5	4
1	2	3	4	5	8	6	7	9
4	5	8	6	7	9	1	2	3
2	1	4	3	6	5	7	9	8
3	8	6	7	9	1	2	4	5
5	9	7	2	8	4	3	1	6
6	3	1	5	4	7	9	8	2
8	4	2	9	1	3	5	6	7
9	7	5	8	2	6	4	3	1

Solution 90

9	7	6	1	8	3	5	2	4
1	2	3	4	5	6	7	8	9
4	5	8	2	7	9	1	3	6
2	1	4	5	3	7	6	9	8
3	6	7	8	9	2	4	5	1
5	8	9	6	4	1	2	7	3
6	3	1	9	2	5	8	4	7
7	4	2	3	1	8	9	6	5
8	9	5	7	6	4	3	1	2

Solution 91

3	6	1	7	4	9	5	8	2
2	4	5	1	3	8	6	7	9
7	8	9	2	5	6	1	3	4
1	2	6	3	7	5	4	9	8
4	3	7	8	9	1	2	5	6
5	9	8	4	6	2	7	1	3
6	1	2	9	8	7	3	4	5
8	5	3	6	1	4	9	2	7
9	7	4	5	2	3	8	6	1

Solution 92

8	2	1	3	6	4	7	5	9
3	5	7	1	2	9	4	6	8
4	6	9	5	7	8	1	2	3
1	3	4	2	5	6	8	9	7
2	7	6	8	9	1	3	4	5
5	9	8	4	3	7	2	1	6
6	1	2	9	8	3	5	7	4
7	4	3	6	1	5	9	8	2
9	8	5	7	4	2	6	3	1

Solution 93

6	3	9	2	1	5	8	4	7
1	2	4	3	7	8	5	6	9
5	7	8	4	6	9	1	2	3
2	1	5	6	3	4	7	9	8
3	8	6	5	9	7	2	1	4
4	9	7	8	2	1	3	5	6
7	4	1	9	5	3	6	8	2
8	5	2	7	4	6	9	3	1
9	6	3	1	8	2	4	7	5

Solution 94

6	8	5	1	3	2	9	7	4
1	2	3	4	7	9	5	6	8
4	7	9	5	6	8	1	2	3
2	1	6	3	4	5	7	8	9
3	4	7	9	8	6	2	1	5
5	9	8	2	1	7	4	3	6
7	3	1	6	5	4	8	9	2
8	5	2	7	9	3	6	4	1
9	6	4	8	2	1	3	5	7

Solution 95

7	9	5	1	3	2	6	4	8
1	2	3	4	6	8	5	7	9
4	6	8	5	7	9	1	2	3
2	1	6	3	4	5	8	9	7
3	4	7	9	8	1	2	5	6
5	8	9	6	2	7	4	3	1
6	3	1	2	9	4	7	8	5
8	5	2	7	1	3	9	6	4
9	7	4	8	5	6	3	1	2

Solution 96

7	8	1	4	9	6	3	2	5
2	4	6	1	3	5	7	8	9
3	5	9	2	7	8	1	4	6
1	2	3	5	4	7	6	9	8
4	6	7	3	8	9	5	1	2
5	9	8	6	2	1	4	3	7
6	1	2	9	5	3	8	7	4
8	3	4	7	6	2	9	5	1
9	7	5	8	1	4	2	6	3

Solution 97

6	2	8	9	3	7	4	1	5
1	3	4	2	5	6	7	8	9
5	7	9	1	4	8	2	3	6
2	1	5	3	7	4	6	9	8
3	8	6	5	2	9	1	4	7
4	9	7	6	8	1	3	5	2
7	4	1	8	9	2	5	6	3
8	5	2	4	6	3	9	7	1
9	6	3	7	1	5	8	2	4

Solution 98

5	4	1	2	6	7	9	3	8
2	3	8	1	4	9	5	6	7
6	7	9	3	5	8	1	2	4
1	2	5	4	3	6	7	8	9
3	8	6	9	7	1	4	5	2
4	9	7	5	8	2	6	1	3
7	1	2	6	9	3	8	4	5
8	5	3	7	1	4	2	9	6
9	6	4	8	2	5	3	7	1

Solution 99

8	1	6	7	4	2	9	3	5
2	3	4	1	5	9	6	7	8
5	7	9	3	6	8	1	2	4
1	2	5	4	3	6	7	8	9
3	6	7	8	9	5	4	1	2
4	9	8	2	1	7	5	6	3
6	4	1	5	2	3	8	9	7
7	5	2	9	8	1	3	4	6
9	8	3	6	7	4	2	5	1

Solution 100

6	4	2	5	3	7	1	8	9
1	3	8	2	4	9	5	6	7
5	7	9	1	6	8	2	3	4
2	1	5	3	7	4	6	9	8
3	8	6	9	2	1	4	7	5
4	9	7	6	8	5	3	2	1
7	2	1	4	9	3	8	5	6
8	5	3	7	1	6	9	4	2
9	6	4	8	5	2	7	1	3

Solution 101

4	8	2	6	7	5	9	1	3
1	3	5	2	4	9	6	7	8
6	7	9	1	3	8	2	4	5
2	1	6	3	5	4	7	8	9
3	4	7	9	8	2	5	6	1
5	9	8	7	1	6	4	3	2
7	2	1	5	6	3	8	9	4
8	5	3	4	9	7	1	2	6
9	6	4	8	2	1	3	5	7

Solution 102

7	3	2	1	9	5	4	8	6
1	4	6	2	3	8	5	7	9
5	8	9	4	6	7	1	2	3
2	1	5	3	4	6	7	9	8
3	6	7	9	8	1	2	5	4
4	9	8	5	7	2	6	3	1
6	2	1	8	5	9	3	4	7
8	5	3	7	1	4	9	6	2
9	7	4	6	2	3	8	1	5

Solution 103

7	8	9	4	5	6	3	2	1
4	5	6	1	2	3	7	8	9
1	2	3	7	8	9	4	5	6
2	1	4	5	3	7	6	9	8
3	6	7	2	9	8	5	1	4
5	9	8	6	4	1	2	7	3
6	3	1	9	7	2	8	4	5
8	4	2	3	1	5	9	6	7
9	7	5	8	6	4	1	3	2

Solution 104

7	8	1	5	6	4	9	2	3
2	4	5	1	3	9	6	7	8
3	6	9	2	7	8	1	4	5
1	2	6	3	4	5	7	8	9
4	3	7	9	8	2	5	1	6
5	9	8	6	1	7	2	3	4
6	1	2	4	5	3	8	9	7
8	5	3	7	9	1	4	6	2
9	7	4	8	2	6	3	5	1

Solution 105

1	4	3	5	7	6	8	2	9
2	8	9	1	3	4	5	6	7
5	6	7	2	8	9	1	3	4
3	1	2	4	6	5	7	9	8
4	7	5	8	9	2	3	1	6
6	9	8	3	1	7	2	4	5
7	2	1	6	4	8	9	5	3
8	3	4	9	5	1	6	7	2
9	5	6	7	2	3	4	8	1

Solution 106

6	9	4	5	8	3	7	2	1
1	3	5	2	4	7	6	8	9
2	7	8	1	6	9	3	4	5
3	1	6	7	2	4	5	9	8
4	2	7	8	9	5	1	6	3
5	8	9	6	3	1	4	7	2
7	4	1	9	5	8	2	3	6
8	5	2	3	7	6	9	1	4
9	6	3	4	1	2	8	5	7

Solution 107

8	2	1	3	5	7	9	6	4
3	4	6	1	2	9	5	7	8
5	7	9	4	6	8	1	2	3
1	3	5	2	4	6	7	8	9
2	6	7	8	9	3	4	1	5
4	9	8	5	7	1	2	3	6
6	1	2	9	8	5	3	4	7
7	5	3	6	1	4	8	9	2
9	8	4	7	3	2	6	5	1

Solution 108

4	9	3	1	8	7	2	5	6
1	2	5	3	4	6	7	8	9
6	7	8	2	5	9	1	3	4
2	1	6	7	3	4	5	9	8
3	4	7	5	9	8	6	1	2
5	8	9	6	2	1	4	7	3
7	3	1	9	6	2	8	4	5
8	5	2	4	1	3	9	6	7
9	6	4	8	7	5	3	2	1

Solution 109

3	1	4	6	2	7	5	8	9
2	5	8	1	3	9	4	6	7
6	7	9	4	5	8	1	2	3
1	2	3	5	4	6	7	9	8
4	8	6	9	7	1	2	3	5
5	9	7	3	8	2	6	1	4
7	3	1	2	9	5	8	4	6
8	4	2	7	6	3	9	5	1
9	6	5	8	1	4	3	7	2

Solution 110

3	8	1	2	6	5	7	9	4
2	4	7	1	3	9	5	6	8
5	6	9	4	7	8	1	2	3
1	2	3	5	4	7	6	8	9
4	7	5	9	8	6	2	3	1
6	9	8	3	2	1	4	5	7
7	1	2	6	9	3	8	4	5
8	3	4	7	5	2	9	1	6
9	5	6	8	1	4	3	7	2

Solution 111

7	8	5	2	1	9	3	6	4
1	2	3	4	5	6	7	8	9
4	6	9	3	7	8	1	2	5
2	1	6	7	3	4	5	9	8
3	4	7	8	9	5	2	1	6
5	9	8	6	2	1	4	7	3
6	3	1	5	8	2	9	4	7
8	5	2	9	4	7	6	3	1
9	7	4	1	6	3	8	5	2

Solution 112

9	6	3	8	4	7	5	1	2
1	2	4	3	5	6	7	8	9
5	7	8	1	2	9	3	4	6
2	1	6	4	3	5	9	7	8
3	5	7	2	9	8	1	6	4
4	8	9	6	7	1	2	3	5
6	3	1	5	8	2	4	9	7
7	4	2	9	6	3	8	5	1
8	9	5	7	1	4	6	2	3

Solution 113

9	1	4	7	8	2	6	3	5
2	3	5	1	4	6	7	8	9
6	7	8	3	5	9	1	2	4
1	2	6	4	3	7	5	9	8
3	5	7	6	9	8	2	4	1
4	8	9	5	2	1	3	6	7
5	4	1	8	6	3	9	7	2
7	6	2	9	1	4	8	5	3
8	9	3	2	7	5	4	1	6

Solution 114

9	7	4	6	3	2	8	1	5
1	2	3	4	5	8	6	7	9
5	6	8	1	7	9	2	3	4
2	1	6	3	4	5	7	9	8
3	5	7	8	9	6	1	4	2
4	8	9	2	1	7	3	5	6
6	3	1	5	2	4	9	8	7
7	4	2	9	8	1	5	6	3
8	9	5	7	6	3	4	2	1

Solution 115

9	6	1	2	5	7	3	4	8
2	3	5	1	4	8	6	7	9
4	7	8	3	6	9	1	2	5
1	2	6	4	3	5	8	9	7
3	4	7	9	8	1	2	5	6
5	8	9	6	7	2	4	1	3
6	1	2	5	9	3	7	8	4
7	5	3	8	1	4	9	6	2
8	9	4	7	2	6	5	3	1

Solution 116

2	8	6	5	4	1	3	9	7
1	3	4	2	7	9	5	6	8
5	7	9	3	6	8	1	2	4
3	1	5	4	2	6	7	8	9
4	2	7	8	9	5	6	3	1
6	9	8	1	3	7	2	4	5
7	4	1	6	8	2	9	5	3
8	5	2	9	1	3	4	7	6
9	6	3	7	5	4	8	1	2

Solution 117

7	3	5	6	9	2	4	1	8
1	2	4	3	5	8	6	7	9
6	8	9	1	4	7	2	3	5
2	1	6	4	3	5	8	9	7
3	5	7	2	8	9	1	6	4
4	9	8	7	1	6	3	5	2
5	4	1	9	2	3	7	8	6
8	6	2	5	7	1	9	4	3
9	7	3	8	6	4	5	2	1

Solution 118

1	9	8	3	6	5	4	2	7
2	3	5	1	4	7	6	8	9
4	6	7	2	8	9	1	3	5
3	1	2	4	5	6	7	9	8
5	7	4	9	1	8	2	6	3
6	8	9	7	3	2	5	1	4
7	2	1	5	9	3	8	4	6
8	4	3	6	7	1	9	5	2
9	5	6	8	2	4	3	7	1

Solution 119

3	8	2	7	5	1	4	6	9
1	4	6	2	3	9	5	7	8
5	7	9	4	6	8	1	2	3
2	1	5	3	4	6	8	9	7
4	3	7	9	8	2	6	1	5
6	9	8	1	7	5	2	3	4
7	2	1	5	9	4	3	8	6
8	5	3	6	1	7	9	4	2
9	6	4	8	2	3	7	5	1

Solution 120

2	3	8	4	7	6	9	5	1
1	4	5	2	3	9	6	7	8
6	7	9	1	5	8	2	3	4
3	1	2	6	4	5	7	8	9
4	8	6	7	9	1	3	2	5
5	9	7	3	8	2	1	4	6
7	2	1	5	6	4	8	9	3
8	5	3	9	1	7	4	6	2
9	6	4	8	2	3	5	1	7

Solution 121

3	6	9	5	8	2	4	1	7
1	2	5	3	4	7	6	8	9
4	7	8	1	6	9	2	3	5
2	1	3	4	5	6	7	9	8
5	8	4	9	7	3	1	2	6
6	9	7	2	1	8	5	4	3
7	3	1	6	9	4	8	5	2
8	4	2	7	3	5	9	6	1
9	5	6	8	2	1	3	7	4

Solution 122

3	6	8	9	1	7	5	4	2
1	2	4	3	5	6	7	8	9
5	7	9	2	4	8	1	3	6
2	1	3	4	7	5	6	9	8
4	8	5	6	9	3	2	1	7
6	9	7	1	8	2	4	5	3
7	3	1	5	6	9	8	2	4
8	4	2	7	3	1	9	6	5
9	5	6	8	2	4	3	7	1

Solution 123

4	2	6	9	7	1	8	3	5
1	3	5	2	4	8	6	7	9
7	8	9	3	5	6	1	2	4
2	1	4	6	3	5	7	9	8
3	6	7	4	8	9	2	5	1
5	9	8	1	2	7	4	6	3
6	4	1	5	9	2	3	8	7
8	5	2	7	1	3	9	4	6
9	7	3	8	6	4	5	1	2

Solution 124

5	1	6	4	8	2	7	9	3
2	3	4	1	7	9	5	6	8
7	8	9	3	5	6	1	2	4
1	2	5	7	3	4	6	8	9
3	6	7	2	9	8	4	5	1
4	9	8	5	6	1	2	3	7
6	4	1	8	2	3	9	7	5
8	5	2	9	1	7	3	4	6
9	7	3	6	4	5	8	1	2

Solution 125

3	6	2	9	5	4	1	7	8
1	4	7	2	3	8	5	6	9
5	8	9	1	6	7	2	3	4
2	1	3	5	4	6	8	9	7
4	7	5	3	8	9	6	1	2
6	9	8	7	1	2	4	5	3
7	2	1	4	9	5	3	8	6
8	3	4	6	7	1	9	2	5
9	5	6	8	2	3	7	4	1

Solution 126

9	6	7	3	5	4	8	1	2
3	4	5	1	2	8	6	7	9
1	2	8	6	7	9	3	4	5
2	1	3	5	4	6	7	9	8
4	7	6	8	9	1	5	2	3
5	8	9	2	3	7	1	6	4
6	3	1	4	8	2	9	5	7
7	5	2	9	1	3	4	8	6
8	9	4	7	6	5	2	3	1

Solution 127

5	7	2	9	1	6	4	8	3
1	3	4	2	5	8	6	7	9
6	8	9	3	4	7	1	2	5
2	1	6	4	3	5	7	9	8
3	5	7	6	8	9	2	4	1
4	9	8	7	2	1	3	5	6
7	2	1	8	9	3	5	6	4
8	4	3	5	6	2	9	1	7
9	6	5	1	7	4	8	3	2

Solution 128

3	9	2	1	5	7	6	8	4
1	4	6	2	3	8	5	7	9
5	7	8	4	6	9	1	2	3
2	1	5	3	4	6	7	9	8
4	3	7	8	9	1	2	5	6
6	8	9	5	7	2	3	4	1
7	2	1	9	8	3	4	6	5
8	5	3	6	2	4	9	1	7
9	6	4	7	1	5	8	3	2

Solution 129

1	6	8	2	9	5	7	4	3
2	3	5	1	4	7	6	8	9
4	7	9	3	6	8	1	2	5
3	1	2	4	7	6	5	9	8
5	8	4	9	1	3	2	7	6
6	9	7	5	8	2	4	3	1
7	2	1	6	3	9	8	5	4
8	4	3	7	5	1	9	6	2
9	5	6	8	2	4	3	1	7

Solution 130

4	5	9	3	7	8	2	6	1
1	2	3	4	5	6	7	8	9
6	7	8	1	2	9	3	4	5
2	1	4	5	3	7	6	9	8
3	8	6	2	9	1	5	7	4
5	9	7	6	8	4	1	3	2
7	3	1	9	4	2	8	5	6
8	4	2	7	6	5	9	1	3
9	6	5	8	1	3	4	2	7

Solution 131

7	6	4	9	3	2	1	8	5
1	2	3	4	5	8	6	7	9
5	8	9	1	6	7	2	3	4
2	1	6	3	4	5	7	9	8
3	5	7	2	8	9	4	1	6
4	9	8	7	1	6	3	5	2
6	3	1	8	9	4	5	2	7
8	4	2	5	7	1	9	6	3
9	7	5	6	2	3	8	4	1

Solution 132

5	1	3	6	9	4	8	7	2
2	4	7	1	3	8	5	6	9
6	8	9	2	5	7	1	3	4
1	2	5	3	4	6	7	9	8
3	7	6	5	8	9	2	4	1
4	9	8	7	1	2	6	5	3
7	3	1	4	2	5	9	8	6
8	5	2	9	6	3	4	1	7
9	6	4	8	7	1	3	2	5

Solution 133

9	3	1	7	8	2	6	4	5
2	4	5	1	3	6	7	8	9
6	7	8	4	5	9	1	2	3
1	2	6	3	4	7	5	9	8
3	5	7	2	9	8	4	1	6
4	8	9	5	6	1	2	3	7
5	1	2	9	7	3	8	6	4
7	6	3	8	1	4	9	5	2
8	9	4	6	2	5	3	7	1

Solution 134

1	7	4	8	9	2	5	3	6
2	3	5	1	4	6	7	8	9
6	8	9	3	5	7	1	2	4
3	1	6	2	7	5	4	9	8
4	2	7	9	6	8	3	1	5
5	9	8	4	3	1	6	7	2
7	4	1	5	2	9	8	6	3
8	5	2	6	1	3	9	4	7
9	6	3	7	8	4	2	5	1

Solution 135

4	3	1	7	6	9	2	8	5
2	5	8	1	3	4	6	7	9
6	7	9	2	5	8	1	3	4
1	2	4	3	7	6	5	9	8
3	8	6	5	9	1	4	2	7
5	9	7	4	8	2	3	1	6
7	1	2	9	4	5	8	6	3
8	4	3	6	1	7	9	5	2
9	6	5	8	2	3	7	4	1

Solution 136

8	9	2	3	6	1	7	5	4
1	3	4	2	5	7	6	8	9
5	6	7	4	8	9	1	2	3
2	1	6	7	3	4	5	9	8
3	5	8	1	9	6	2	4	7
4	7	9	5	2	8	3	1	6
6	2	1	8	4	3	9	7	5
7	4	3	9	1	5	8	6	2
9	8	5	6	7	2	4	3	1

Solution 137

8	3	5	7	9	1	6	4	2
1	2	4	3	5	6	7	8	9
6	7	9	2	4	8	1	3	5
2	1	6	4	3	7	5	9	8
3	5	7	1	8	9	2	6	4
4	9	8	5	6	2	3	1	7
5	4	1	8	2	3	9	7	6
7	6	2	9	1	4	8	5	3
9	8	3	6	7	5	4	2	1

Solution 138

6	4	5	9	8	2	1	7	3
1	2	3	4	5	7	6	8	9
7	8	9	1	3	6	2	4	5
2	1	6	3	4	5	7	9	8
3	5	7	2	9	8	4	1	6
4	9	8	6	7	1	3	5	2
5	3	1	8	2	4	9	6	7
8	6	2	7	1	9	5	3	4
9	7	4	5	6	3	8	2	1

Solution 139

6	2	5	9	3	4	1	8	7
1	3	4	2	7	8	5	6	9
7	8	9	1	5	6	2	3	4
2	1	6	3	4	5	7	9	8
3	5	7	6	8	9	4	1	2
4	9	8	7	2	1	6	5	3
5	4	1	8	9	7	3	2	6
8	6	2	4	1	3	9	7	5
9	7	3	5	6	2	8	4	1

Solution 140

6	7	3	4	9	5	1	2	8
1	4	5	2	3	8	6	7	9
2	8	9	1	6	7	3	4	5
3	1	6	5	2	4	8	9	7
4	2	7	8	1	9	5	6	3
5	9	8	6	7	3	2	1	4
7	3	1	9	5	2	4	8	6
8	5	2	7	4	6	9	3	1
9	6	4	3	8	1	7	5	2

Solution 141

9	2	8	7	4	5	1	6	3
1	4	5	2	3	6	7	8	9
3	6	7	1	8	9	2	4	5
2	1	3	4	5	7	6	9	8
4	7	6	9	2	8	3	5	1
5	8	9	3	6	1	4	2	7
6	3	1	5	9	2	8	7	4
7	5	2	8	1	4	9	3	6
8	9	4	6	7	3	5	1	2

Solution 142

6	2	3	8	4	9	1	5	7
1	4	5	2	3	7	6	8	9
7	8	9	1	5	6	2	3	4
2	1	6	3	7	4	5	9	8
3	5	7	9	8	1	4	6	2
4	9	8	5	6	2	3	7	1
5	3	1	4	9	8	7	2	6
8	6	2	7	1	3	9	4	5
9	7	4	6	2	5	8	1	3

Solution 143

7	1	9	3	2	4	8	6	5
2	3	5	1	6	8	4	7	9
4	6	8	5	7	9	1	2	3
1	2	4	6	3	5	7	9	8
3	8	6	7	9	1	2	5	4
5	9	7	4	8	2	6	3	1
6	4	1	2	5	3	9	8	7
8	5	2	9	1	7	3	4	6
9	7	3	8	4	6	5	1	2

Solution 144

8	7	4	6	5	9	3	1	2
1	5	6	2	3	4	7	8	9
2	3	9	1	7	8	4	5	6
3	1	2	5	4	7	6	9	8
4	6	7	8	9	1	5	2	3
5	9	8	3	2	6	1	7	4
6	2	1	4	8	5	9	3	7
7	4	3	9	1	2	8	6	5
9	8	5	7	6	3	2	4	1

Solution 145

4	3	5	8	9	7	1	6	2
1	2	6	3	4	5	7	8	9
7	8	9	1	2	6	3	4	5
2	1	4	5	7	3	6	9	8
3	6	7	4	8	9	5	2	1
5	9	8	6	1	2	4	3	7
6	4	1	9	5	8	2	7	3
8	5	2	7	3	4	9	1	6
9	7	3	2	6	1	8	5	4

Solution 146

8	4	7	3	6	5	9	1	2
1	3	5	2	4	9	6	7	8
2	6	9	1	7	8	3	4	5
3	1	2	4	5	6	7	8	9
4	7	6	8	9	2	1	5	3
5	9	8	7	1	3	2	6	4
6	2	1	5	3	4	8	9	7
7	5	3	9	8	1	4	2	6
9	8	4	6	2	7	5	3	1

Solution 147

4	5	8	3	9	7	2	1	6
1	2	3	4	5	6	7	8	9
6	7	9	1	2	8	3	4	5
2	1	4	7	3	5	6	9	8
3	8	6	2	4	9	5	7	1
5	9	7	6	8	1	4	2	3
7	3	1	9	6	2	8	5	4
8	4	2	5	1	3	9	6	7
9	6	5	8	7	4	1	3	2

Solution 148

5	2	8	1	9	3	6	7	4
1	3	4	2	6	7	5	8	9
6	7	9	4	5	8	1	2	3
2	1	5	3	4	6	7	9	8
3	8	6	7	1	9	2	4	5
4	9	7	5	8	2	3	1	6
7	4	1	9	3	5	8	6	2
8	5	2	6	7	4	9	3	1
9	6	3	8	2	1	4	5	7

Solution 149

9	7	8	4	6	3	2	5	1
3	4	6	1	2	5	7	8	9
1	2	5	7	8	9	3	4	6
2	1	3	5	4	7	6	9	8
4	6	7	2	9	8	1	3	5
5	8	9	3	1	6	4	7	2
6	3	1	9	5	4	8	2	7
7	5	2	8	3	1	9	6	4
8	9	4	6	7	2	5	1	3

Solution 150

1	2	8	6	9	4	3	5	7
3	4	5	1	2	7	6	8	9
6	7	9	3	5	8	1	2	4
2	1	3	5	4	6	7	9	8
4	8	6	7	1	9	5	3	2
5	9	7	2	8	3	4	6	1
7	3	1	9	6	2	8	4	5
8	5	2	4	3	1	9	7	6
9	6	4	8	7	5	2	1	3

Solution 151

2	8	4	3	1	5	6	9	7
1	3	6	2	7	9	4	5	8
5	7	9	4	6	8	1	2	3
3	1	5	6	2	4	7	8	9
4	2	7	9	8	3	5	6	1
6	9	8	1	5	7	3	4	2
7	4	1	5	9	2	8	3	6
8	5	2	7	3	6	9	1	4
9	6	3	8	4	1	2	7	5

Solution 152

3	9	4	5	6	8	2	1	7
1	2	5	3	4	7	6	8	9
6	7	8	1	2	9	3	4	5
2	1	6	4	3	5	7	9	8
4	3	7	9	8	2	5	6	1
5	8	9	7	1	6	4	2	3
7	4	1	2	9	3	8	5	6
8	5	2	6	7	1	9	3	4
9	6	3	8	5	4	1	7	2

Solution 153

1	4	9	3	6	2	5	7	8
2	3	5	1	7	8	4	6	9
6	7	8	4	5	9	1	2	3
3	1	2	5	4	6	8	9	7
4	8	6	7	9	1	3	5	2
5	9	7	2	8	3	6	1	4
7	2	1	6	3	4	9	8	5
8	5	3	9	1	7	2	4	6
9	6	4	8	2	5	7	3	1

Solution 154

4	2	1	6	5	7	9	8	3
3	8	9	1	2	4	5	6	7
5	6	7	3	8	9	1	2	4
1	3	4	2	6	5	8	7	9
2	7	5	4	9	8	3	1	6
6	9	8	7	3	1	2	4	5
7	1	2	5	4	3	6	9	8
8	4	3	9	1	6	7	5	2
9	5	6	8	7	2	4	3	1

Solution 155

1	2	5	8	3	7	4	9	6
3	4	6	1	2	9	5	7	8
7	8	9	4	5	6	1	2	3
2	1	3	6	4	5	7	8	9
4	6	7	2	9	8	3	1	5
5	9	8	3	7	1	2	6	4
6	3	1	7	8	4	9	5	2
8	5	2	9	1	3	6	4	7
9	7	4	5	6	2	8	3	1

Solution 156

7	2	9	6	4	1	3	8	5
1	3	4	2	5	8	6	7	9
5	6	8	3	7	9	1	2	4
2	1	5	4	3	6	7	9	8
3	8	6	7	9	5	4	1	2
4	9	7	8	1	2	5	3	6
6	4	1	9	2	3	8	5	7
8	5	2	1	6	7	9	4	3
9	7	3	5	8	4	2	6	1